To Zackary
love
memme
1993

A COLLECTION OF
ANIMAL
STORIES

A COLLECTION OF
ANIMAL
STORIES

HAMLYN

First published in 1980
This revised edition published in 1991 by
Hamlyn Children's Books, part of Reed International Books,
Michelin House, 81 Fulham Road, London SW3 6RB

This arrangement copyright © 1980, 1991
Octopus Books Limited

First edition edited by Anthea Ridett
Line illustrations by Sally Stiff
Cover artwork by Alan Fraser (represented by David Lewis)

ISBN 0 600 57094 0

Printed in England

Contents

ADOLF

D.H. Lawrence

When we were children our father often worked on the night-shift.
Once it was spring-time, and he used to arrive home, black and tired,
just as we were downstairs in our nightdresses. Then night met
morning face to face, and the contact was not always happy. Perhaps
it was painful to my father to see us gaily entering upon the day into
which he dragged himself soiled and weary. He didn't like going to bed
in the spring morning sunshine.

But sometimes he was happy, because of his long walk through the
dewy fields in the first daybreak. He loved the open morning, the
crystal and the space, after a night down pit. He watched every bird,
every stir in the trembling grass, answered the whinnying of the peewits
and tweeted to the wrens. If he could, he also would have whinnied and
tweeted and whistled in a native language that was not human. He
liked non-human things best.

One sunny morning we were all sitting at table when we heard his
heavy slurring walk up the entry. We became uneasy. His was always a
disturbing presence, trammelling. He passed the window darkly, and
we heard him go into the scullery and put down his tin bottle. But
directly he came into the kitchen. We felt at once that he had something

to communicate. No one spoke. We watched his black face for a second.

'Give me a drink,' he said.

My mother hastily poured out his tea. He went to pour it out into his saucer. But instead of drinking he suddenly put something on the table among the teacups. A tiny brown rabbit! A small rabbit, a mere morsel, sitting against the bread as still as if it were a made thing.

'A rabbit! A young one! Who gave it you, Father?'

But he laughed enigmatically, with a sliding motion of his yellow-grey eyes, and went to take off his coat. We pounced on the rabbit.

'Is it alive? Can you feel its heart beat?'

My father came back and sat down heavily in his armchair. He dragged his saucer to him, and blew his tea, pushing out his red lips under his black moustache.

'Where did you get it, Father?'

'I picked it up,' he said, wiping his naked forearm over his mouth and beard.

'Where?'

'It is a wild one!' came my mother's quick voice.

'Yes it is.'

'Then why did you bring it?' cried my mother.

'Oh, we wanted it', came our cry.

'Yes, I've no doubt you did—' retorted my mother. But she was drowned in our clamour of questions.

On the field path my father had found a dead mother rabbit and three dead little ones—this one alive, but unmoving.

'But what had killed them, Daddy?'

'I couldn't say, my child. I s'd think she'd aten something.'

'Why did you bring it!' again my mother's voice of condemnation. 'You know what it will be.'

My father made no answer, but we were loud in protest.

'He must bring it. It's not big enough to live by itself. It would die,' we shouted.

'Yes, and it will die now. And then there'll be *another* outcry.'

My mother set her face against the tragedy of dead pets. Our hearts sank.

'It won't die, Father, will it? Why will it? It won't.'

7

'I s'd think not,' said my father.

'You know well enough it will. Haven't we had it all before!' said my mother.

'They dunna always pine,' replied my father testily.

But my mother reminded him of other little wild animals he had brought, which had sulked and refused to live, and brought storms of tears and trouble in our house of lunatics.

Trouble fell on us. The little rabbit sat on our lap, unmoving, its eye wide and dark. We brought it milk, warm milk, and held it to its nose. It sat still as if it was far away, retreated down some deep burrow, hidden, oblivious. We wetted its mouth and whiskers with drops of milk. It gave no sign, did not even shake off the wet white drops. Somebody began to shed a few secret tears.

'What did I say?' cried my mother. 'Take it and put it down in the field.'

Her command was in vain. We were driven to get dressed for school. There sat the rabbit. It was like a tiny obscure cloud. Watching it, the emotions died out of our breast. Useless to love it, to yearn over it. Its little feelings were all ambushed. They must be circumvented. Love and affection were a trespass upon it. A little wild thing, it became more mute and asphyxiated still in its own arrest, when we approached with love. We must not love it. We must circumvent it, for its own existence.

So I passed the order to my sister and my mother. The rabbit was not to be spoken to, nor even looked at. Wrapping it in a piece of flannel I put it in an obscure corner of the cold parlour, and put a saucer of milk before its nose. My mother was forbidden to enter the parlour while we were at school.

'As if I should take any notice of your nonsense,' she cried affronted. Yet I doubt if she ventured into the parlour.

At midday, after school, creeping into the front room, there we saw the rabbit still and unmoving in the piece of flannel. Strange grey-brown neutralization of life, still living! It was a sore problem to us.

'Why won't it drink its milk, Mother?' we whispered. Our father was asleep.

'It prefers to sulk its life away, silly little thing.' A profound problem. Prefers to sulk its life away! We put young dandelion

8

leaves to its nose. The sphinx was not more oblivious. Yet its eye was bright.

At tea-time, however, it had hopped a few inches, out of its flannel, and there it sat again, uncovered, a little solid cloud of muteness, brown, with unmoving whiskers. Only its side palpitated slightly with life.

Darkness came; my father set off to work. The rabbit was still unmoving. Dumb despair was coming over the sisters, a threat of tears before bed-time. Clouds of my mother's anger gathered as she muttered against my father's wantonness.

Once more the rabbit was wrapped in the old pit-singlet. But now it was carried into the scullery and put under the copper fire-place, that it might imagine itself inside a burrow. The saucers were placed about, four or five, here and there on the floor, so that if the little creature *should* chance to hop abroad, it could not fail to come upon some food. After this my mother was allowed to take from the scullery what she wanted and then she was forbidden to open the door.

When morning came and it was light, I went downstairs. Opening the scullery door, I heard a slight scuffle. Then I saw dabbles of milk all over the floor and tiny rabbit droppings in the saucers. And there the miscreant, the tips of his ears showing behind a pair of boots. I peeped at him. He sat bright-eyed and askance, twitching his nose and looking at me while not looking at me.

He was alive—very much alive. But still we were afraid to trespass much on his confidence.

'Father!' My father was arrested at the door. 'Father, the rabbit's alive.'

'Back your life it is,' said my father.

'Mind how you go in.'

By evening, however, the little creature was tame, quite tame. He was christened Adolf. We were enchanted by him. We couldn't really love him, because he was wild and loveless to the end. But he was an unmixed delight.

We decided he was too small to live in a hutch—he must live at large in the house. My mother protested, but in vain. He was so tiny. So we had him upstairs, and he dropped his tiny pills on the bed and we were enchanted.

Adolf made himself instantly at home. He had the run of the house, and was perfectly happy, with his tunnels and his holes behind the furniture.

We loved him to take meals with us. He would sit on the table humping his back, sipping his milk, shaking his whiskers and his tender ears, hopping off and hobbling back to his saucer, with an air of supreme unconcern. Suddenly he was alert. He hobbled a few tiny paces, and reared himself up inquisitively at the sugar basin. He fluttered his tiny fore-paws, and then reached and laid them on the edge of the basin, while he craned his thin neck and peeped in. He trembled his whiskers at the sugar, then he did his best to lift down a lump.

'*Do* you think I will have it! Animals in the sugar pot!' cried my mother, with a rap of her hand on the table.

Which so delighted the electric Adolf that he flung his hind-quarters and knocked over a cup.

'It's your own fault, Mother. If you left him alone—'

He continued to take tea with us. He rather liked warm tea. And he loved sugar. Having nibbled a lump, he would turn to the butter. There he was shooed off by our parent. He soon learned to treat her shooing with indifference. Still, she hated him to put his nose in the food. And he loved to do it. And one day between them they over-turned the cream-jug. Adolf deluged his little chest, bounced back in terror, was seized by his little ears by my mother and bounced down on the hearth-rug. There he shivered in momentary discomfort, and suddenly set off in a wild flight to the parlour.

This was his happy hunting ground. He had cultivated the bad habit of pensively nibbling certain bits of cloth in the hearth-rug. When chased from this pasture he would retreat under the sofa. There he would twinkle in Buddhist meditation until suddenly, no one knew why, he would go off like an alarm clock. With a sudden bumping scuffle he would whirl out of the room, going through the doorway with his little ears flying. Then we would hear his thunderbolt hurtling in the parlour, but before we could follow, the wild streak of Adolf would flash past us, on an electric wind that swept him round the scullery and carried him back, a little mad thing, flying possessed like a ball round the parlour. After which ebullition he would sit in a corner composed and distant, twitching his whiskers in abstract meditation.

Suddenly he put a tiny, brown rabbit amidst the teacups.

And it was in vain we questioned him about his outburst. He just went off like a gun, and was as calm after it as a gun that smokes placidly.

Alas, he grew up rapidly. It was almost impossible to keep him from the outer door.

One day, as we were playing by the stile, I saw his brown shadow loiter across the road and pass into the field that faced the houses. Instantly a cry of 'Adolf!'—a cry he knew full well. And instantly a wind swept him away down the sloping meadow, his tail twinkling and zigzagging through the grass. After him we pelted. It was a strange sight to see him, ears back, his little loins so powerful, flinging the world behind him. We ran ourselves out of breath, but could not catch him. Then somebody headed him off, and he sat with sudden unconcern, twitching his nose under a bunch of nettles.

His wanderings cost him a shock. One Sunday morning my father had just been quarrelling with a pedlar, and we were hearing the aftermath indoors, when there came a sudden unearthly scream from the yard. We flew out. There sat Adolf cowering under a bench, while a great black and white cat glowered intently at him, a few yards away. Sight not to be forgotten. Adolf rolling back his eyes and parting his strange muzzle in another scream, the cat stretching forward in a slow elongation.

Ha, how we hated that cat! How we pursued him over the chapel wall and across the neighbours' gardens.

Adolf was still only half grown.

'Cats!' said my mother. 'Hideous detestable animals, why do people harbour them?'

But Adolf was becoming too much for her. He dropped too many pills. And suddenly to hear him clumping downstairs when she was alone in the house was startling. And to keep him from the door was impossible. Cats prowled outside. It was worse than having a child to look after.

Yet we would not have him shut up. He became more lusty, more callous than ever. He was a strong kicker, and many a scratch on face and arms did we owe to him. But he brought his own doom on himself. The lace curtains in the parlour—my mother was rather proud of them—fell on the floor very full. One of Adolf's joys was to scuffle wildly through them as though through some foamy undergrowth. He had already torn rents in them.

One day he entangled himself altogether. He kicked, he whirled round in a mad nebulous inferno. He screamed—and brought down the curtain-rod with a smash, right on the best beloved pelargonium, just as my mother rushed in. She extricated him, but she never forgave him. And he never forgave either. A heartless wildness had come over him.

Even we understood that he must go. It was decided, after a long deliberation, that my father should carry him back to the wild-woods. Once again he was stowed into the great pocket of the pit-jacket.

'Best pop him i' th' pot,' said my father, who enjoyed raising the wind of indignation.

And so, next day, our father said that Adolf, set down on the edge of the coppice, had hopped away with utmost indifference, neither elated nor moved. We heard it and believed. But many, many were the heartsearchings. How would the other rabbits receive him? Would they smell his tameness, his humanized degradation, and rend him? My mother pooh-poohed the extravagant idea.

However, he was gone, and we were rather relieved. My father kept an eye open for him. He declared that several times passing the coppice in the early morning, he had seen Adolf peeping through the nettle-stalks. He had called him, in an odd-voiced, cajoling fashion. But Adolf had not responded. Wildness gains so soon upon its creatures. And they become so contemptuous then of our tame presence. So it seemed to me. I myself would go to the edge of the coppice, and call softly. I myself would imagine bright eyes between the nettle-stalks, flash of a white, scornful tail past the bracken. That insolent white tail, as Adolf turned his flank on us!

THE NIGHTINGALE AND THE ROSE

Oscar Wilde

'She said that she would dance with me if I brought her red roses,' cried the young Student, 'but in all my garden there is no red rose.'

From her nest in the holm-oak tree the Nightingale heard him, and she looked out through the leaves and wondered.

'No red rose in all my garden!' he cried, and his beautiful eyes filled with tears. 'Ah, on what little things does happiness depend! I have read all that the wise men have written, and all the secrets of philosophy are mine, yet for want of a red rose is my life made wretched.'

'Here at last is a true lover,' said the Nightingale. 'Night after night have I sung of him though I knew him not: night after night have I told his story to the stars and now I see him. His hair is dark as the hyacinth-blossom, and his lips are red as the rose of his desire, but passion has made his face like pale ivory and sorrow has set her seal upon his brow.'

'The Prince gives a ball tomorrow night,' murmured the young Student, 'and my love will be of the company. If I bring her a red rose she will dance with me till dawn. If I bring her a red rose, I shall hold her in my arms, and she will lean her head upon my shoulder and her hand will be clasped in mine. But there is no red rose in my garden, so

I shall sit lonely and she will pass me by. She will have no heed of me, and my heart will break.'

'Here, indeed, is the true lover,' said the Nightingale. 'What I sing of, he suffers: what is joy to me, to him is pain. Surely love is a wonderful thing. It is more precious than emeralds and dearer than fine opals. Pearls and pomegranates cannot buy it, nor is it set forth in the market-place. It may not be purchased of the merchants, nor can it be weighed out in the balance for gold.'

'The musicians will sit in their gallery,' said the young Student, 'and play upon their stringed instruments, and my love will dance to the sound of the harp and the violin. She will dance so lightly that her feet will not touch the floor, and the courtiers in their gay dresses will throng round her. But with me she will not dance, for I have no red rose to give her'; and he flung himself down on the grass, and buried his face in his hands, and wept.

'Why is he weeping?' asked a little Green Lizard, as he ran past him with his tail in the air.

'Why, indeed?' said the Butterfly, who was fluttering about after a sunbeam.

'Why, indeed?' whispered a Daisy to his neighbour, in a soft, low voice.

'He is weeping for a red rose,' said the Nightingale.

'For a red rose?' they cried; 'how very ridiculous!' and the little Lizard, who was something of a cynic, laughed outright.

But the Nightingale understood the secret of the Student's sorrow, and she sat silent in the oak-tree, and thought about the mystery of Love.

Suddenly she spread her brown wings for flight, and soared into the air. She passed through the grove like a shadow and like a shadow she sailed across the garden.

In the centre of the grass-plot was standing a beautiful rose-tree, and when she saw it she flew over to it, and lit upon a spray.

'Give me a red rose,' she cried, 'and I will sing you my sweetest song.'

But the Tree shook its head.

'My roses are white,' it answered; 'as white as the foam of the sea, and whiter than the snow on the mountain. But go to my brother who grows round the old sun-dial, and perhaps he will give you what you want.'

So the Nightingale flew over to the Rose-tree that was growing round the old sun-dial.

'Give me a red rose,' she cried, 'and I will sing you my sweetest song.'

But the Tree shook its head.

'My roses are yellow,' it answered; 'as yellow as the hair of the mermaiden who sits upon an amber throne, and yellower than the daffodil that blooms in the meadow before the mower comes with his scythe. But go to my brother who grows beneath the Student's window, and perhaps he will give you what you want.'

So the Nightingale flew over to the Rose-tree that was growing beneath the Student's window.

'Give me a red rose,' she cried, 'and I will sing you my sweetest song.'

But the Tree shook its head.

'My roses are red,' it answered; 'as red as the feet of the dove, and redder than the great fans of coral that wave and wave in the ocean-cavern. But the winter has chilled my veins, and the frost has nipped my buds, and the storm has broken my branches, and I shall have no roses at all this year.'

'One red rose is all I want,' cried the Nightingale, 'only one red rose! Is there no way by which I can get it?'

'There is a way,' answered the Tree, 'but it is so terrible that I dare not tell it to you.'

'Tell it to me,' said the Nightingale, 'I am not afraid.'

'If you want a red rose,' said the Tree, 'you must build it out of music by moonlight, and stain it with your own heart's-blood. You must sing to me with your breast against a thorn. All night long you must sing to me, and the thorn must pierce your heart, and your life-blood must flow into my veins, and become mine.'

'Death is a great price to pay for a red rose,' cried the Nightingale, 'and Life is very dear to all. It is pleasant to sit in the green wood, and to watch the Sun in his chariot of gold, and the Moon in her chariot of pearl. Sweet is the scent of the hawthorn, and sweet are the bluebells that hide in the valley, and the heather that blows on the hill. Yet Love is better than Life, and what is the heart of a bird compared to the heart of a man?'

So she spread her brown wings for flight, and soared into the air. She swept over the garden like a shadow, and like a shadow she sailed through the grove.

The young Student was still lying on the grass, where she had left him, and the tears were not yet dry in his beautiful eyes.

'Be happy,' cried the Nightingale, 'be happy; you shall have your red rose. I will build it out of music by moonlight, and stain it with my own heart's-blood. All that I ask of you in return is that you will be a true lover, for Love is wiser than Philosophy, though he is wise, and mightier than Power, though he is mighty. Flame-coloured are his wings, and coloured like flame is his body. His lips are sweet as honey, and his breath is like frankincense.'

The Student looked up from the grass, and listened, but he could not understand what the Nightingale was saying to him, for he only knew the things that are written down in books.

But the Oak-tree understood, and felt sad, for he was very fond of the little Nightingale who had built her nest in his branches.

'Sing me one last song,' he whispered; 'I shall feel lonely when you are gone.'

So the Nightingale sang to the Oak-tree, and her voice was like water bubbling from a silver jar.

When she had finished her song, the Student got up, and pulled a note-book and a lead-pencil out of his pocket.

'She has form,' he said to himself, as he walked away through the grove—'that cannot be denied to her; but has she got feeling? I am afraid not. In fact, she is like most artists; she is all style without any sincerity. She would not sacrifice herself for others. She thinks merely of music, and everybody knows that the arts are selfish. Still, it must be admitted that she has some beautiful notes in her voice. What a pity it is that they do not mean anything, or do any practical good!' And he went into his room, and lay down on his little pallet-bed, and began to think of his love; and, after a time, he fell asleep.

And when the moon shone in the heavens the Nightingale flew to the Rose-tree, and set her breast against the thorn. All night long she sang, with her breast against the thorn, and the cold crystal Moon leaned down and listened. All night long she sang, and the thorn went deeper and deeper into her breast, and her life-blood ebbed away from her.

And when the student opened his window he found the beautiful, red rose.

She sang first of the birth of love in the heart of a boy and a girl. And on the topmost spray of the Rose-tree there blossomed a marvellous rose, petal following petal, as song followed song. Pale was it, at first, as the mist that hangs over the river—pale as the feet of the morning, and silver as the wings of the dawn. As the shadow of a rose in a mirror of silver, as the shadow of a rose in a waterpool, so was the rose that blossomed on the topmost spray of the Tree.

But the Tree cried to the Nightingale to press closer against the thorn. 'Press closer, little Nightingale,' cried the Tree, 'or the Day will come before the rose is finished.'

So the Nightingale pressed closer against the thorn, and louder and louder grew her song, for she sang of the birth of passion in the soul of a man and a maid.

And a delicate flush of pink came into the leaves of the rose, like the flush in the face of the bridegroom when he kisses the lips of the bride. But the thorn had not yet reached her heart, so the rose's heart remained white, for only a Nightingale's heart's-blood can crimson the heart of a rose.

And the Tree cried to the Nightingale to press closer against the thorn. 'Press closer, little Nightingale,' cried the Tree, 'or the Day will come before the rose is finished.'

So the Nightingale pressed closer against the thorn, and the thorn touched her heart, and a fierce pang of pain shot through her. Bitter, bitter was the pain, and wilder and wilder grew her song, for she sang of the Love that is perfected by Death, of the Love that dies not in the tomb.

And the marvellous rose became crimson, like the rose of the eastern sky. Crimson was the girdle of petals, and crimson as a ruby was the heart.

But the Nightingale's voice grew fainter, and her little wings began to beat, and a film came over her eyes. Fainter and fainter grew her song, and she felt something choking in her throat.

Then she gave one last burst of music. The white Moon heard it, and she forgot the dawn, and lingered on in the sky. The red rose heard it, and it trembled all over with ecstasy, and opened its petals to the cold morning air. Echo bore it to her purple cavern in the hills, and woke the sleeping shepherds from their dreams. It floated through the reeds of the river, and they carried its message to the sea.

'Look, look!' cried the Tree, 'the rose is finished now'; but the Nightingale made no answer, for she was lying dead in the long grass, with the thorn in her heart.

And at noon the Student opened his window and looked out.

'Why, what a wonderful piece of luck!' he cried; 'here is a red rose! I have never seen any rose like it in all my life. It is so beautiful that I am sure it has a long Latin name'; and he leaned down and plucked it.

Then he put on his hat, and ran up to the Professor's house with the rose in his hand.

The daughter of the Professor was sitting in the door-way winding blue silk on a reel, and her little dog was lying at her feet.

'You said that you would dance with me if I brought you a red rose,' cried the Student. 'Here is the reddest rose in all the world. You will wear it tonight next your heart, and as we dance together it will tell you how I love you.'

But the girl frowned.

'I am afraid it will not go with my dress,' she answered; 'and, besides, the Chamberlain's nephew has sent me some real jewels, and everybody knows that jewels cost far more than flowers.'

'Well, upon my word, you are very ungrateful,' said the Student angrily; and he threw the rose into the street, where it fell into the gutter, and a cart-wheel went over it.

'Ungrateful!' said the girl. 'I tell you what, you are very rude; and, after all, who are you? Only a Student. Why, I don't believe you have even got silver buckles to your shoes as the Chamberlain's nephew has'; and she got up from her chair and went into the house.

'What a silly thing Love is!' said the Student as he walked away. 'It is not half as useful as Logic, for it does not prove anything, and it is always telling one of things that are not going to happen, and making one believe things that are not true. In fact, it is quite unpractical, and, as in this age to be practical is everything, I shall go back to Philosophy and study Metaphysics.'

So he returned to his room and pulled out a great dusty book, and began to read.

THE PIPER AT THE GATES OF DAWN

Kenneth Grahame

The Willow-Wren was twittering his thin little song, hidden himself in the dark selvedge of the river bank. Though it was past ten o'clock at night, the sky still clung to and retained some lingering skirts of light from the departed day; and the sullen heats of the torrid afternoon broke up and rolled away at the dispersing touch of the cool fingers of the short midsummer night. Mole lay stretched on the bank, still panting from the stress of the fierce day that had been cloudless from dawn to late sunset, and waited for his friend to return. He had been on the river with some companions, leaving the Water Rat free to keep an engagement of long standing with Otter; and he had come back to find the house dark and deserted, and no sign of Rat, who was doubtless keeping it up late with his old comrade. It was still too hot to think of staying indoors, so he lay on some cool dock-leaves, and thought over the past day and its doings, and how very good they all had been.

The Rat's light footfall was presently heard approaching over the parched grass. 'O, the blessed coolness!' he said, and sat down, gazing thoughtfully into the river, silent and preoccupied.

'You stayed to supper, of course?' said the Mole presently.

'Simply had to,' said the Rat. 'They wouldn't hear of my going before. You know how kind they always are. And they made things as jolly for me as ever they could, right up to the moment I left. But I felt a brute all the time, as it was clear to me they were very unhappy, though they tried to hide it. Mole, I'm afraid they're in trouble. Little Portly is missing again; and you know what a lot his father thinks of him, though he never says much about it.'

'What, that child?' said the Mole lightly. 'Well, suppose he is; why worry about it? He's always straying off and getting lost, and turning up again; he's so adventurous. But no harm ever happens to him. Everybody hereabouts knows him and likes him, just as they do old Otter, and you may be sure some animal or other will come across him and bring him back again all right. Why, we've found him ourselves, miles from home and quite self-possessed and cheerful!'

'Yes; but this time it's more serious,' said the Rat gravely. 'He's been missing for some days now, and the Otters have hunted every-where, high and low, without finding the slightest trace. And they've asked every animal, too, for miles around, and no one knows anything about him. Otter's evidently more anxious than he'll admit. I got out of him that young Portly hasn't learnt to swim very well yet, and I can see he's thinking of the weir. There's a lot of water coming down still, considering the time of year, and the place always had a fascination for the child. And then there are—well, traps and things—*you* know. Otter's not the fellow to be nervous about any son of his before it's time. And now he *is* nervous. When I left, he came out with me—said he wanted some air, and talked about stretching his legs. But I could see it wasn't that, so I drew him out and pumped him, and got it all from him at last. He was going to spend the night watching by the ford. You know the place where the old ford used to be, in bygone days before they built the bridge?'

'I know it well,' said the Mole. 'But why should Otter choose to watch there?'

'Well, it seems that it was there he gave Portly his first swimming lesson,' continued the Rat. 'From that shallow, gravelly spit near the bank. And it was there he used to teach him fishing, and there young Portly caught his first fish, of which he was very proud. The child loved the spot, and Otter thinks that if he came wandering back from wherever he is—if he *is* anywhere by this time, poor little chap—he might make for the ford he was so fond of; or if he came across it he'd remember it well, and stop there and play, perhaps. So Otter goes there every night and watches—on the chance, you know, just on the chance!'

They were silent for a time, both thinking of the same thing—the lonely, heart-sore animal, crouched by the ford, watching and waiting, the long night through—on the chance.

'Well, well,' said the Rat presently, 'I suppose we ought to be thinking about turning in.' But he never offered to move.

'Rat,' said the Mole, 'I simply can't go and turn in, and go to sleep, and *do* nothing, even though there doesn't seem to be anything to be done. We'll get the boat out, and paddle up-stream. The moon will be up in an hour or so, and then we will search as well as we can—anyhow, it will be better than going to bed and doing *nothing*.'

'Just what I was thinking myself,' said the Rat. 'It's not the sort of night for bed anyhow; and daybreak is not so far off, and then we may pick up some news of him from early risers as we go along.'

They got the boat out, and the Rat took the sculls, paddling with caution. Out in mid-stream there was a clear, narrow track that faintly reflected the sky; but wherever shadows fell on the water from bank, bush, or tree, they were as solid to all appearance as the banks themselves, and the Mole had to steer with judgement accordingly. Dark and deserted as it was, the night was full of small noises, song and chatter and rustling, telling of the busy little population who were up and about, plying their trades and vocations through the night till sunshine should fall on them at last and send them off to their well-earned repose. The water's own noises, too, were more apparent than by day, its gurglings and 'cloops' more unexpected and near at hand; and constantly they started at what seemed a sudden clear call from an actual articulate voice.

The line of the horizon was clear and hard against the sky, and in one particular quarter it showed black against a silvery climbing phosphorescence that grew and grew. At last, over the rim of the waiting earth the moon lifted with slow majesty till it swung clear of the horizon and rode off, free of moorings; and once more they began to see surfaces—meadows widespread, and quiet gardens, and the river itself from bank to bank, all softly disclosed, all washed

The Rat and Mole stood worshipping at the Piper's feet.

clean of mystery and terror, all radiant again as by day, but with a difference that was tremendous. Their old haunts greeted them again in other raiment, as if they had slipped away and put on this pure new apparel and come quietly back, smiling as they shyly waited to see if they would be recognized again under it.

Fastening their boat to a willow, the friends landed in this silent, silver kingdom, and patiently explored the hedges, the hollow trees, the tunnels and their little culverts, the ditches and dry water-ways. Embarking again and crossing over, they worked their way up the stream in this manner, while the moon, serene and detached in a cloudless sky, did what she could, though so far off, to help them in their quest; till her hour came and she sank earthwards reluctantly, and left them, and mystery once more held field and river.

Then a change began slowly to declare itself. The horizon became clearer, field and tree came more into sight, and somehow with a different look; the mystery began to drop away from them. A bird piped suddenly, and was still; and a light breeze sprang up and set the reeds and bulrushes rustling. Rat, who was in the stern of the boat, while Mole sculled, sat up suddenly and listened with a passionate intentness. Mole, who with gentle strokes was just keeping the boat moving while he scanned the banks with care, looked at him with curiosity.

'It's gone!' sighed the Rat, sinking back in his seat again. 'So beautiful and strange and new! Since it was to end so soon, I almost wish I had never heard it. For it has roused a longing in me that is pain, and nothing seems worthwhile but just to hear that sound once more and go on listening to it for ever. No! There it is again!' he cried, alert once more. Entranced, he was silent for a long space, spellbound.

'Now it passes on and I begin to lose it,' he said presently. 'O, Mole! the beauty of it! The merry bubble and joy, the thin, clear, happy call of the distant piping! Such music I never dreamed of, and the call in it is stronger even than the music is sweet! Row on, Mole, row! For the music and the call must be for us.'

The Mole, greatly wondering, obeyed. 'I hear nothing myself,' he said, 'but the wind playing in the reeds and rushes and osiers.'

The Rat never answered, if indeed he heard. Rapt, transported, trembling, he was possessed in all his senses by this new divine thing that caught up his helpless soul and swung and dandled it, a powerless but happy infant, in a strong sustaining grasp.

In silence Mole rowed steadily, and soon they came to a point where the river divided, a long backwater branching off to one side. With a slight movement of his head Rat, who had long dropped the rudder-lines, directed the rower to take the backwater. The creeping tide of light gained and gained, and now they could see the colour of the flowers that gemmed the water's edge.

'Clearer and nearer still,' cried the Rat joyously. 'Now you must surely hear it! Ah—at last—I see you do!'

Breathless and transfixed the Mole stopped rowing as the liquid run of that glad piping broke on him like a wave, caught him up, and possessed him utterly. He saw the tears on his comrade's cheeks, and bowed his head and understood. For a space they hung there, brushed by the purple loosestrife that fringed the bank; then the clear imperious summons that marched hand-in-hand with the intoxicating melody imposed its will on Mole, and mechanically he bent to his oars again. And the light grew steadily stronger, but no birds sang as they were wont to do at the approach of dawn; and but for the heavenly music all was marvellously still.

On either side of them, as they glided onwards, the rich meadow-grass seemed that morning of a freshness and a greeness unsurpassable. Never had they noticed the roses so vivid, the willow-herb so riotous, the meadow-sweet so odorous and pervading. Then the murmur of the approaching weir began to hold the air, and they felt a consciousness that they were nearing the end, whatever it might be, that surely awaited their expedition.

A wide half-circle of foam and glinting lights and shining shoulders of green water, the great weir closed the backwater from bank to bank, troubled all the quiet surface with twirling eddies and floating foam-streaks, and deadened all other sounds with its solemn and soothing rumble. In midmost of the stream, embraced in the weir's shimmering arm-spread, a small island lay anchored, fringed close with willow and silver birch and alder. Reserved, shy, but full of significance, it hid whatever it might hold behind a veil, keeping it till the hour should come, and, with the hour, those who were called and chosen.

Slowly, but with no doubt or hesitation whatever, and in something of a solemn expectancy, the two animals passed through the broken, tumultuous water and moored their boat at the flowery margin of the island. In silence they landed, and pushed through the blossom and scented herbage and undergrowth that led up to the level ground, till they stood on a little lawn of a marvellous green, set round with Nature's own orchard-trees—crab-apples, wild cherry, and sloe.

'This is the place the music played to me,' whispered the Rat, as if in a trance. 'Here, in this holy place, here if anywhere, surely we shall find Him!'

Then suddenly the Mole felt a great Awe fall upon him, an awe that turned his muscles to water, bowed his head, and rooted his feet to the ground. It was no panic terror—indeed he felt wonderfully at peace and happy—but it was an awe that smote and held him and, without seeing, he knew it could only mean that some august Presence was very, very near. With difficulty he turned to look for his friend, and saw him at his side cowed, stricken, and trembling violently. And still there was utter silence in the populous bird-haunted branches around them; and still the light grew and grew.

Perhaps he would never have dared to raise his eyes, but that, though the piping was now hushed, the call and the summons seemed still dominant and imperious. He might not refuse, were Death himself waiting to strike him instantly, once he had looked with mortal eye on things rightly kept hidden. Trembling he obeyed, and raised his humble head; and then, in that utter clearness of the imminent dawn, while Nature, flushed with fullness of incredible colour, seemed to hold her breath for the event, he looked in the very eyes of the Friend and Helper; saw the backward sweep of the curved horns, gleaming in the growing daylight; saw the stern, hooked nose between the kindly eyes that were looking down on them humorously, while the bearded mouth broke into a half-smile at the corners; saw the rippling muscles on the arm that lay across the broad chest, the long supple hand still holding the pan-pipes only just fallen away from the parted lips; saw the splendid curves of the shaggy limbs disposed in majestic ease on the sward; saw, last of all, nestling between his very hooves, sleeping soundly in entire peace and contentment, the little, round, podgy, childish form of the baby otter. All this he saw, for one

27

moment breathless and intense, vivid on the morning sky; and still, as he looked, he lived; and still, as he lived, he wondered.

'Rat!' he found breath to whisper, shaking. 'Are you afraid?'

'Afraid?' murmured the Rat, his eyes shining with unutterable love. 'Afraid Of *Him*? O, never, never! And yet—and yet—O, Mole, I am afraid!'

Then the two animals, crouching to the earth, bowed their heads and did worship.

Sudden and magnificent, the sun's broad golden disc showed itself over the horizon facing them; and the first rays, shooting across the level water-meadows, took the animals full in the eyes and dazzled them. When they were able to look once more, the Vision had vanished, and the air was full of the carol of birds that hailed the dawn.

As they stared blankly, in dumb misery deepening as they slowly realized all they had seen and all they had lost, a capricious little breeze, dancing up from the surface of the water, tossed the aspens, shook the dewy roses, and blew lightly and caressingly in their faces, and with its soft touch came instant oblivion. For this is the last best gift that the kindly demigod is careful to bestow on those to whom he has revealed himself in their helping; the gift of forgetfulness. Lest the awful remembrance should remain and grow, and overshadow mirth and pleasure, and the great haunting memory should spoil all the after-lives of little animals helped out of difficulties, in order that they should be happy and light-hearted as before.

Mole rubbed his eyes and stared at Rat, who was looking about him in a puzzled sort of way. 'I beg your pardon; what did you say, Rat?' he asked.

'I think I was only remarking,' said Rat slowly, 'that this was the right sort of place, and that here, if anywhere, we should find him. And look! Why, there he is, the little fellow!' And with a cry of delight he ran towards the slumbering Portly.

But Mole stood still a moment, held in thought. As one wakened suddenly from a beautiful dream, who struggles to recall it, and can recapture nothing but a dim sense of the beauty of it, the beauty! Till that, too, fades away in its turn, and the dreamer bitterly accepts the hard, cold waking and all its penalties; so Mole, after struggling with his memory for a brief space, shook his head sadly and followed the Rat.

Portly woke up with a joyous squeak, and wriggled with pleasure at the sight of his father's friends, who had played with him so often in past days. In a moment, however, his face grew blank, and he fell to hunting round in a circle with pleading whine. As a child that has fallen happily asleep in its nurse's arms, and wakes to find itself alone and laid in a strange place, and searches corners and cupboards, and runs from room to room, despair growing silently in its heart, even so Portly searched the island and searched, dogged and unwearying, till at last the black moment came for giving it up, and sitting down and crying bitterly.

The Mole ran quickly to comfort the little animal; but Rat, lingering, looked long and doubtfully at certain hoof-marks deep in the sward.

'Some—great—animal—has been here,' he murmured slowly and thoughtfully; and stood musing, musing; his mind strangely stirred.

'Come along, Rat!' called the Mole. 'Think of poor Otter, waiting up there by the ford!'

Portly had soon been comforted by the promise of a treat—a jaunt on the river in Mr Rat's real boat; and the two animals conducted him to the water's side, placed him securely between them in the bottom of the boat, and paddled off down the backwater. The sun was fully up by now, and hot on them, birds sang lustily and without restraint, and flowers smiled and nodded from either bank, but somehow—so thought the animals—with less of richness and blaze of colour than they seemed to remember seeing quite recently somewhere—they wondered where.

The main river reached again, they turned the boat's head upstream, towards the point where they knew their friend was keeping his lonely vigil. As they drew near the familiar ford, the Mole took the boat in to the bank, and they lifted Portly out and set him on his legs on the tow-path, gave him his marching orders and a friendly farewell pat on the back, and shoved out into mid-stream. They watched the little animal as he waddled along the path contentedly and with importance; watched him till they saw his muzzle suddenly lift and his waddle break into a clumsy amble as he quickened his pace with shrill whines and wriggles of recognition. Looking up the river, they could see Otter start up, tense and rigid, from out of the shallows where he crouched in dumb patience, and could hear his amazed and joyous bark as he bounded up through the osiers on to the path. Then the Mole, with a strong pull on one oar, swung the boat round and let the full stream bear them down again whither it would, their quest now happily ended.

'I feel strangely tired, Rat,' said the Mole, leaning wearily over his oars as the boat drifted. 'It's being up all night, you'll say, perhaps; but that's nothing. We do as much half the nights of the week, at this time of the year. No; I feel as if I had been through something very exciting and rather terrible, and it was just over; and yet nothing particular has happened.'

'Or something very surprising and splendid and beautiful,' murmured the Rat, leaning back and closing his eyes. 'I feel just as you do, Mole; simply dead tired, though not body-tired. It's lucky we've got the stream with us, to take us home. Isn't it jolly to feel the sun again, soaking into one's bones! And hark to the wind playing in the reeds!'

'It's like music—far-away music,' said the Mole, nodding drowsily.

'So I was thinking,' murmured the Rat, dreamful and languid. 'Dance-music—the lilting sort that runs on without a stop—but with words in it, too—it passes into words and out of them again—I catch them at intervals—then it is dance-music once more, and then nothing but the reeds' soft thin whispering.'

'You hear better than I,' said the Mole sadly. 'I cannot catch the words.'

'Let me try and give you them,' said the Rat softly, his eyes still closed. 'Now it is turning into words again—faint but clear—*Lest the awe should dwell—And turn your frolic to fret—You shall look on my power at the helping hour—But then you shall forget!* Now the reeds take it up—*forget, forget,* they sigh, and it dies away in a rustle and a whisper. Then the voice returns—

'*Lest limbs be reddened and rent—I spring the trap that is set—As I loose the snare you may glimpse me there—For surely you shall forget!* Row nearer, Mole, nearer to the reeds! It is hard to catch, and grows each minute fainter.

'*Helper and healer, I cheer—Small waifs in the woodland wet—Strays*

I find in it, wounds I bind in it—Bidding them all forget! Nearer, Mole, nearer! No, it is no good; the song has died away into reed-talk.'

'But what do the words mean?' asked the wondering Mole.

'That I do not know,' said the Rat simply. 'I passed them on to you as they reached me. Ah! now they return again, and this time full and clear! This time, at last, it is the real, the unmistakable thing, simple—passionate—perfect—'

'Well, let's have it then,' said the Mole, after he had waited patiently for a few minutes, half dozing in the hot sun.

But no answer came. He looked, and understood the silence. With a smile of much happiness on his face, and something of a listening look still lingering there, the weary Rat was fast asleep.

THE MIRACLE CLIMB

Gerald Durrell

The fauna of Australia is something that makes any self-respecting naturalist excited. It has been described by one person as 'the attic of the world', the place where all the old things are stored; this is quite an apt description but is not strictly accurate. The two most interesting orders in Australia are the monotremes and the marsupials. The monotremes are the most primitive of mammals and have retained many of the characteristics which prove how mammals are descended from the reptiles. Superficially, the monotremes resemble conventional mammals in the sense that they breathe air, they are covered with fur, and they are warm blooded, but their chief and most astonishing reptilian characteristic is the fact that they lay eggs, and then, when the young hatch from the eggs, the parents feed them on milk. Most famous of the monotremes, of course, is the Duck-Billed Platypus.

The marsupials are remarkable for a number of characteristics, best known of which is, of course, that the majority of them have a very short gestation period and give birth to their young in an almost embryonic condition. The baby then finds its way to the mother's pouch and continues its development from there. The marsupials are very primitive creatures and it is lucky for them that the land bridge over which they spread into Australia was destroyed, for the more conventional mammals (such as tigers, leopards, lions and so on) would have made short work of them. However, cut off as they were, with this great continent to themselves, they evolved along the most amazing lines—a sort of parallel evolution took place; instead of the great herds of hoofed animals that developed in Africa, Asia and America, you get the kangaroos and wallabies, who filled the same grazing niche. The places occupied by bushbabies or squirrels in other parts of the world were occupied in Australia by Possums and phalangers. A creature like the Badger has its equivalent in Australia in the Wombat, and the predators are represented by such things as the Tasmanian Wolf—not a true wolf, of course, but a marsupial, looking remarkably like its counterpart. So not only did the marsupials adapt themselves to the various niches but they came to resemble, in habits and sometimes in appearance, totally unrelated creatures that had evolved in other parts of the world: thus, the little Honey-Eaters look, at first glance, exactly like some of the smaller species of mouse; the Wombat resembles the Badger; the Tasmanian Wolf a member of the dog family, and there is even a Banded Anteater, to complete the picture. As an example of evolution the continent of Australia, with its monotremes and marsupials, is just as extraordinary as the Galapagos Islands, which so excited Darwin's imagination that he evolved the whole evolutionary thesis.

By and large, before the coming of man the marsupials had a pretty idyllic set-up. Then came the aborigines and with them (one suspects) came the Dingo, a very cunning predator who rapidly became, together with his owners, the aborigines, Public Enemy Number One to the fauna. Although the Dingoes multiplied and spread, they did not appear to upset the balance of nature very much; neither did the aborigines, for there were too few of them, but with the advent of white men, the picture became very much blacker for the marsupials. Not only were their numbers depleted by human beings, but their habitat was invaded by introduced creatures such as the European fox and rabbit, the fox on the one hand acting as predator and the rabbit acting as competition to the grazing marsupials for the food. Then came the sheep, and this is where the larger grazing marsupials started to acquire a bad reputation, for now they were in competition with the sheep and the sheep was more important to man. The farmers opened up whole new areas which, prior to this, had been arid and unsuitable country even for kangaroos and wallabies, and by driving wells and bore-holes they produced lush pastures for their sheep. They also found, to their annoyance, that the kangaroos and wallabies were deeply appreciative of this and poured into these new areas in numbers equalling, and in some cases exceeding, the sheep. So what is called the 'kangaroo menace' came into being.

Before you can control any wild animal, you have to know something about its basic biology; a simple policy of slaughter—quite apart from its threat to the survival of that particular species—is liable to do untold damage to the whole ecological structure of the country. An unbiological approach in different parts of the world to problems of this sort has, in the past, proved disastrous. So if an animal is becoming a pest you must set to work to learn everything you can about it; it is a case of 'knowing thine enemy'. The Wildlife Department of the CSIRO was set up with just this object in mind. As soon as an animal is proclaimed a pest, the CSIRO moves in and investigates the whole problem. They have to act, really, in the capacity of a High Court Judge, because in many cases a creature has been labelled a pest, and upon investigation, has proved to be considerably less of a pest than was thought. At Canberra, the CSIRO have a large laboratory where one of their major studies at the moment is the two species of kangaroo—the Great Red and the Great Grey—so it was here that we went to get first-hand information on what would be the ultimate fate of the two largest and most spectacular marsupials in the world.

The team is headed by Harry Frith, who is one of Australia's foremost biologists and, among other things, famous for his brilliant ecological studies of various Australian ducks and geese and the Mallee-Fowl. He is a stocky, curly-haired man, his face browned and seamed by the sun and wind, the possessor of the most cynically amused pair of eyes I have seen for a long time, and of a dry, caustic and deceptively laconic approach towards his work. When I suggested that we would like to do some film sequences of their work, Harry stared at me moodily.

'I'll take you down to the yards,' he said, 'and introduce you to the boys. I don't mind you doing some film sequences but it's up to the boys. They're all working hard and it would mean they would have to waste a certain amount of time with you, so the decision must rest with them. If they tell you to push off, I can't do anything about it.' Then he smiled encouragingly at me.

Hoping that 'the boys' were going to be a trifle less misanthropic, we followed him down to the yards, which were a series of paddocks in which various species of kangaroo and wallaby were kept and bred. Here we were introduced to Geoff Sharman, a tall and utterly charming Australian scientist who is probably one of the world's foremost authorities on the biology of the marsupial. Having, as it were, pushed us into the lion's den, Harry then retreated to get on with his work, leaving me to try to make my mark with Geoff Sharman. This, to my relief, proved far easier than I had been led to anticipate; not only was Geoff a charming person, but so enthusiastic over his work that anybody who evinced the slightest interest in it became somebody worth talking to.

'We're looking for information that can be used for assessing the wild animals we find in the field. In other words, we're measuring the young in the pouch to see how they grow, and from this we can build up growth curves, which can be used to tell the age of the wild-caught young ones,' Geoff explained to me. 'We're also looking at their teeth. This is very important because the eruption pattern of the teeth seems to be a good way of telling the age of a kangaroo. This will give us some idea of the actual age structure of any population we are dealing with in the wilds. Once we've found that out here, the next thing is to go out and get a wild population of kangaroos marked in some way so that we can identify them. Then we examine their teeth every time we capture them, and see if we get the same kind of eruption pattern in the wild animal.'

'What's the breeding potentiality of a female kangaroo?' I asked him.

'Terrific,' Geoff said. 'It's like a Ford production belt. She can have one growing inside her, one in the pouch fastened to a teat and another one out of the pouch but still feeding from her.'

I asked him about the actual birth of the kangaroo, a thing that had always fascinated me, and it was at this juncture that he dropped his bomb-shell.

'Oh, the *birth*,' he said casually, 'I've got a bit of film I can show you of that.'

I stood rooted to the spot and stared at him.

'You've actually filmed it?' I said incredulously, 'but I thought that very few people had ever witnessed a birth, let alone got it on film.'

'Well, I think we're the first to get it on film,' he said. 'But we've got it down to quite a fine art here. We can tell you to within a few hours when the female is going to give birth.'

Chris and Jacquie were further down the yards, making love through the wire to an enchanting and precious wallaby. I rushed down to Chris.

'Chris, do you know what Geoff Sharman's just told me?'

'What?' said Chris without interest, continuing his love-making with the wallaby.

'He's just told me that he's got some film of the actual birth of a kangaroo!'

'Oh?' said Chris, somewhat mystified by my obvious excitement, and appearing to be under the impression that to have a piece of film of a kangaroo birth was most commonplace. 'So what?'

'What do you mean, so what?' I said. 'You moron, don't you realize that very few people have ever *seen* a kangaroo birth, and I didn't think anyone had ever *filmed* it. In fact, I think that Geoff is probably the first person to do so.'

'Um,' said Chris, brightening a little, 'is it very interesting?'

'Well, of course it's interesting,' I said. 'The thing's only about the size of a hazlenut when it's born—it's virtually an embryo, in fact, and once it's born it then has to climb all the way up its mother and get into the pouch.'

'That sounds as though it would make a good sequence,' said Chris, displaying more enthusiasm. 'I wonder if Geoff would let us use his film?'

We went over to where Geoff had extracted a hairless and rather revolting-looking baby kangaroo from its mother's pouch and was solemnly weighing it in a cloth bag.

'Geoff,' I said wheedlingly, 'is there any chance of you letting us have that piece of film on the kangaroo birth?'

36

'Sure,' he said instantly, and then dampened my hopes by adding, 'but you'll have to check with Harry first.'

'Oh yes,' I said, 'I'll do that, but look, if the film for some reason is not suitable, is there a chance of our re-shooting it?'

'Oh yes,' said Geoff, 'that's easy enough, we've got several females that will be ready fairly soon, but again I can't let you do that without permission from Harry.'

'But,' I said, getting things quite clear, 'you'd have no objection to our doing it providing Harry says it's okay?'

'None at all,' said Geoff. 'I'd be glad to help.'

We had arranged to meet Harry for lunch and during it I cunningly kept off the subject of marsupial births until Harry had engulfed several lamb chops and a couple of pints of beer and was beginning to look a little bit benign round the edges. Then I took a deep breath, and started.

'Harry, Geoff Sharman tells me that you have some film of a kangaroo birth,' I said.

Harry eyed me inimically.

'Yes,' he said cautiously.

'I suppose it wouldn't be possible for us to have a print of that to include in the series?' I said.

'I don't see why not,' said Harry, 'but I'm afraid the decision must rest with Geoff.'

'Oh,' I said, 'well that's all right then, he has already said yes, but he had to have your confirmation.'

Harry ruminated on this and there was a faint twinkle in his eye.

'But supposing,' I said, hastily pouring him out another glass of beer, 'that the film is not entirely suitable for television?'

'Well,' said Harry, 'let's suppose it, what then?'

'Well, would it be possible to re-shoot it?'

'I presume,' said Harry dryly, 'that you've already got Geoff Sharman's permission for this?'

'Well, in a tentative sort of way,' I admitted, 'but he said that you'd have to give the final word.'

'I don't mind,' said Harry. 'If Geoff feels he can fit it in with his work and if he can organize it for you, I don't mind a bit.'

I heaved a deep sigh of relief and beamed at Christopher.

'This, dear boy,' I said, 'is going to be the climax of the series. If we get it!'

After lunch we went jubilantly back to Geoff Sharman to tell him that Harry had agreed. Geoff was delighted and had very soon fixed up a projector in his room in order to show us the coveted piece of film. This, however, proved disappointing, for although it showed the details that were of importance from Geoff's point of view as a scientist, it was unsuitable for television. This meant that we would have to put into operation Plan Two, which was to re-film the whole thing.

'I think Pamela is probably our best bet,' said Geoff, staring at a doe-eyed Grey Kangaroo who was busy picking up pieces of carrot in her monkey-like front paws and chewing them vigorously. 'She is due in about a week's time and, anyway, if we fail with her we can fall back on Marilyn or Marlene, who should be giving birth shortly afterwards.'

'What's the drill then?' I asked.

'Well, the first signs,' said Geoff, 'are that she starts to clean out the pouch. This generally happens a few hours before the birth itself. If you are somewhere within easy reach, we can 'phone you and it will give you time to set up the lights and the cameras.'

'Won't the camera and lights worry her?' asked Chris.

'I shouldn't think so for a moment,' said Geoff, 'she's a very placid creature.'

So began a period of waiting, while we hovered round Pamela like expectant fathers, filming her every move. But we wanted to try to show the full picture of the kangaroo problem as well as the birth, if we were lucky enough to get it, and so Harry, together with Bevan Bowan, took us out to a 'spread' not far from Canberra (a tiny little smallholding of some 200,000 acres) on which they were investigating another facet of the kangaroo's biology.

'We're endeavouring to find out a number of different things,' said Harry as we bumped our way over the sun-bleached grass in among the eucalyptus trees. 'Firstly, we want to know how the groups of kangaroos move—how much territory they cover in, say, a week or a month. This we can only do by catching them up and marking them, so that they are recognisable from a distance, through field-glasses. We do this by putting a coloured collar on them, with

She was slumped in the corner, oblivious to everything around her.

a number. You'll see how we do it presently. The other thing we are trying to find out is whether or not the kangaroo is a selective feeder. Now take East Africa; there's a country that supports vast quantities of game animals and the reason they haven't turned it into a gigantic dust bowl is because they are selective feeders, so that one species of antelope feeds on a certain series of plants and ignores others, which are, in turn, eaten by a different species of antelope. Where your undermining of the country and the creation of erosion comes in, is when you introduce a species that is an indiscriminate feeder. In East Africa the damage is largely done by the huge herds of skinny and totally unattractive cattle, and flocks of goats which just chew up everything in sight. It's possible that we might find a roughly similar situation here. It's possible that we might find that the kangaroo is a selective feeder and therefore, in fact, does less damage to the country than the rabbit or the sheep, although, of course, if this proves to be so, we are going to have the devil's own job persuading the sheep farmer that this is the case.'

He chuckled reminiscently.

'I remember up north,' he said, 'when I went about telling the rice farmers that the Magpie Goose was not the pest that they claimed, I nearly got lynched on several occasions, and once I was pulled out of my car by a giant of a man, who would have flattened me if it had not been for the fact that I luckily had Bevan with me.'

'I never knew conservation could be so bloodthirsty,' I said.

'You'd be surprised,' said Harry. 'No, but it's quite obvious that the kangaroo is a problem. I've known of farms where the kangaroo population has outnumbered the sheep population by about three to one. Obviously this is detrimental to the sheep farmers' interests and something must be done about it. What we hope to achieve is a control over the kangaroo so that we don't have to exterminate them. I see no reason why, if we can learn to control them successfully, we should not have both kangaroos and sheep.'

We had been driving for some considerable time along the edge of a barbed wire fence and we came now to a curious structure at one corner of this gigantic field. A sort of funnel had been built alongside the fence, using the fence as one wall and wire netting for the other. This funnel led into a small paddock some thirty feet square.

'This,' said Harry, 'is the trap. Now the art of catching the kangaroo is this; first you find your kangaroos and then you chivvy them gently until they're heading along the fence. Gradually you increase speed, but you have to do it very cautiously—if you are too quick, you'll panic them and they'll jump over the fence and get away. You must chivvy them at just the right speed to keep them on the go so they'll hop right down that fence, through the funnel and into that trap, and then you've got to run like hell to catch them before they jump out of the trap.'

He leant out of the window to shout some instructions to Bevan, who was driving the other Land-Rover, and then both vehicles were off, circling the paddock, searching for the kangaroos. Travelling at 35 miles an hour over that bumpy terrain, swerving in and out of the eucalyptus trees, was quite a hair-raising experience. The first creatures we disturbed were a flock of Emus, who behaved in a fairly typically stupid manner. Instead of breaking away from us, they seemed so panic-stricken and fascinated that they ran to try to cut across our bows. Having got just in front of us, they then appeared to become quite hysterical and incapable of running to one side, and thumped along in front of us, their great feet almost touching their chins in their efforts to out-run us. Presently we came to a fence and, to my astonishment, the Emus made no effort to stop, but just ran straight at it. One went through, leaving a cloud of feathers behind him, but the other one struck the barbed wire at an angle and bounced off. He staggered back and then took another run at it, and this time he was successful, although he, too, left enough feathers behind him to stuff a small cushion.

'That's why the farmers don't like Emus, either,' said Harry, 'they do the hell of a lot of damage to the fences.'

We progressed for about another quarter of an hour, then suddenly heard Bevan honking his horn. Looking over, we saw a flock of about ten Grey Kangaroos sitting stock-still at the edge of a little wood, staring at us with their ears pricked. Harry swerved violently round a tree to correct our course and we headed straight for the kangaroos, while Bevan drove out further to prevent them from breaking back. As we drew close to them they started hopping off in a rather nonchalant fashion, but as the vehicles accelerated the kangaroos panicked and started running away in real earnest. It was fascinating to watch them taking those prodigious leaps, using their tails purely as a balancing organ. Soon we had chivvied them round so that they were lolloping along the length of the fence towards the trap, and here both vehicles suddenly put on a burst of speed. I would not have thought it was possible to drive through that sort of country at 50 miles an hour, but we did it. The kangaroos were by now thoroughly panic-stricken, and although some of them stopped and made an attempt to leap the fence, we always managed to prevent them by putting on another burst of speed. At last, the trap came into sight. A final burst of speed from the two Land-Rovers and the panic-stricken kangaroos raced down the funnel and found themselves at a dead end. We clamped on our brakes, leapt out of the Land-Rover and raced down the fence into the trap amongst the milling mob of kangaroos. There is only one way to catch a kangaroo successfully and that is to avoid, at all costs, his massive and potentially lethal hind legs, and grasp him firmly by the tail. He then proceeds to bounce in front of you until he is exhausted or until someone else comes to your rescue and grabs other parts of his anatomy. This we proceeded to do until we had all the kangaroos firmly hogtied. Under the baking sun, the poor things were panting and sweating with the exertion and the heat. Carefully each one was dressed up in a neat, celluloid collar in different colours and with a different number on each, and we took them, one by one, outside the trap and let them go. Most of them hopped away rapidly and with obvious relief, but there was one small one who, when placed on the ground, remained standing stock-still, staring into space. Harry went up behind it and patted it gently on the rump, whereupon the kangaroo turned on him ferociously, and an extremely amusing boxing match took place, with Harry endeavouring to shoo the kangaroo away and the kangaroo endeavouring to get its own back on Harry. As the kangaroo only measured about three feet high and Harry was a good six feet, the marsupial's attacks on him had all the temerity of David's encounter with Goliath. At last, however, it decided that its desire to disembowel Harry was doomed to failure and so, with a certain amount of reluctance, it hopped off to join the others.

It was now getting near the time when we could expect the birth and so we took up residence in a Motel, conveniently situated about half a mile down the road from the laboratories. This was when Pamela decided that she was going to give us a run for our money. For three days she designed a series of false alarms for us, and she timed these so cleverly that they did the maximum amount of damage to our nervous systems. Suddenly, as we were in the middle of lunch, or in the bath, or just drifting cosily off to sleep, there would be a frantic telephone message from Geoff to say he thought, from Pamela's behaviour, that the birth was imminent. If we happened to be bathing or sleeping it meant a frantic scramble into our clothes, a wild gallop into the courtyard with our equipment, and we would pile into the Land-Rover and drive off with a deafening roar. Every time we got down to the yards, however, Pamela would be munching some delicacy and would look up with a faintly surprised air that we should have bothered to pay her yet another visit.

Then came the evening when, in the middle of dinner, the Motel proprietor came galloping into the dining-room and informed us that Geoff Sharman had just 'phoned and said that *quite definitely* Pamela was going to give birth at any minute. Knocking over a bottle of wine and leaving our napkins strewn across the floor like autumn leaves, we fled from the dining-room, pursued by cheers and shouts of 'Good luck' from our fellow guests. Chris, in his eagerness, started the Land-Rover so quickly that I was left with one foot inside and one on the ground when he was changing into top; with a fearful effort that almost dislocated my spine, I managed to scramble in, and we zoomed down the road to the laboratories.

'She's definitely going to do it this time,' said Geoff. 'I'm quite certain of it.'

She couldn't have picked a better time. It was pitch dark, bitterly cold, and everything was drenched in dew. Hastily we rigged up the arc lights and got the cameras in position. Pamela was sitting, leaning against a fence and getting on with the good work of cleaning out her pouch. This she did very fastidiously, using her front paws. The pouch, when untenanted, tends to exude a waxy substance similar to the wax in a human ear, and it was this that she was cleaning out, carefully combing the furry interior of the pouch with her claws. We filmed her doing this and then sat and gazed at her expectantly. She continued cleaning her pouch out for about half an hour, stared round moodily, then hopped down to the far end of the paddock and started to eat.

'I think we've got a little time to wait,' said Geoff.

'Are you quite sure that this isn't another of her false alarms?' I asked.

'Oh no,' said Geoff, 'this is the real thing; she wouldn't clean out her pouch as thoroughly as that if she wasn't going to give birth.'

We sat in the freezing cold and stared at Pamela and she stared back at us, her jaws moving rhythmically.

'Let's go into the hut while we're waiting,' said Geoff, 'it will be a little bit warmer. If your hands get too cold, you won't be able to manipulate your equipment.'

We crowded into the tiny shed, where I produced, to the delight of the assembled company, a bottle of whisky that I had had the foresight to bring with me. We took it in turns, between drinks, to go out and peer hopefully in Pamela's direction.

It came as somewhat of a relief when one of Geoff's assistants appeared in the doorway of the hut and said, 'Action stations, I think we're off.'

We scrambled out of the hut and took up our positions. Pamela was moving about, looking rather uncomfortable. Presently, against the fence of the paddock, she dug a shallow hole in the ground and then took up a position in it, with her tail sticking out between her hind legs and her back resting against the fence. She sat like this for a few minutes and then obviously started feeling uncomfortable again, for she lay down on her side for a few seconds and then stood up and moved around for a bit. Then she went back to the hole she had dug and again sat with her tail sticking out between her legs and her back against the fence. She was completely unperturbed by the fact that arc lights, two cine cameras and the eyes of about a dozen people were fixed on her.

'You'd better start the cameras now,' said Geoff.

The cameras started to whirr and, as if on cue, the baby was born. It dropped out on to Pamela's tail and lay there, a pinky-white, glistening blob no longer than the first joint of my little finger.

Although I knew roughly what to expect, the whole performance was one of the most miraculous and incredible things that I have ever seen in all the years that I have been watching animals. The baby was, to all intents and purposes, an embryo—it had, in fact, been born after a gestation period of only 33 days; it was blind and its hind legs, neatly crossed over each other, were powerless; yet in this condition it had been expelled into the world. As if this was not enough of a handicap, it now had to climb up through the fur on Pamela's stomach until it found the entrance to the pouch. This was really the equivalent of a blind man, with both legs broken, crawling through thick forest to the top of Mount Everest, for the baby got absolutely no assistance from Pamela at all. We noticed (and we have it on film to prove it) that the mother does *not* help the baby by licking a path through the fur, as is so commonly reported. The baby, as soon as it was born, with a curious, almost fish-like wiggle, left the mother's tail and started to struggle up through the fur. Pamela ignored it. She bent over and licked her nether regions and her tail clean and then proceeded to clean her fur *behind* the baby as it was climbing, for it was obviously leaving a trail of moisture through her hair. Occasionally her tongue passed over the baby, but I am certain that this was more by accident than design. Slowly and valiantly the pulsating little pink blob struggled on through the thick fur. From the moment it was born to the moment it found the rim of the pouch took some ten minutes. That a creature weighing only a gramme (the weight of five or six pins) could have achieved this climb was a miracle in itself, but, having got to the rim of the pouch, it had another task ahead of it. The pouch is approximately the size of a large, woman's handbag. Into this the Lilliputian kangaroo had to crawl and then search the vast, furry area in order to find the teat; this search might have taken him anything up to twenty minutes. Having found the teat, he would then fasten on to it, whereupon it would swell in his mouth, thus making him adhere to it firmly—so firmly, indeed, that if you try to pull a baby kangaroo off its mother's teat, you will tear the soft mouth parts and cause bleeding. This has given rise to the entirely erroneous idea that baby kangaroos are born on the teat, i.e. develop from the teat itself, like a sort of bud.

Finally the baby hauled itself over the edge of the rim of the pouch and disappeared into the interior, and we could switch off the cameras and the lights. We had got some remarkable and unique film. For me it had been an unforgettable experience, and I am sure that even the most hardened anti-kangaroo sheep farmer would have been impressed by the baby's grim determination to perform its herculean task.

After being cast out into the world only half-formed, and being made to undertake this prodigious climb, I felt that the baby kangaroo thoroughly deserved his life in his fur-lined, centrally-heated pram with its built-in milk bar. I hoped very sincerely, that the work that was being done by Harry Frith, Geoff Sharman and the other members of the team would find a way to preserve the largest of the marsupials from complete eradication.

HOW THESEUS SLEW THE MINOTAUR

Charles Kingsley

Theseus, the hero of this Greek myth, was the son of Aegeus, King of Athens but was brought up by his mother, Princess Aithra of Troezene. At sixteen, when he was strong enough to lift a heavy rock under which lay his father's sword and sandals, he was told the secret of his birth and sent to Athens to join his father. On the journey his strength and courage were put to use in destroying monsters and punishing tyrants. And even after his arrival, his adventures were not over. In Crete the Minotaur, half-man, half-bull, awaited the yearly tribute demanded by King Minos.

So Theseus stayed with his father all the winter, and when the spring equinox drew near, all the Athenians grew sad and silent, and Theseus saw it, and asked the reason; but no one would answer him a word.

Then he went to his father, and asked him: but Aegeus turned away his face and wept.

'Do not ask, my son, beforehand, about evils which must happen: it is enough to have to face them when they come.'

And when the spring equinox came a herald came to Athens, and stood in the market, and cried: 'O people and King of Athens, where is your yearly tribute?' Then a great lamentation arose throughout the city. But Theseus stood up to the herald, and cried:

'And who are you, dog-faced, who dare demand tribute here? If I did not reverence your herald's staff, I would brain you with this club.'

And the herald answered proudly, for he was a grave and ancient man:

'Fair youth, I am not dog-faced or shameless; but I do my master's bidding, Minos, the King of hundred-citied Crete, the wisest of all kings on earth. And you must surely be a stranger here, or you would know why I come, and that I come by right.'

'I am a stranger here. Tell me then why you come.'

'To fetch the tribute which King Aegeus promised to Minos, and confirmed his promise with an oath. For Minos conquered all this land, and Megara which lies to the west, when he came hither with a great fleet of ships, enraged about the murder of his son. For his son Androgeos came hither to the Panathenaic games, and overcame all the Greeks in the sports, so that the people honoured him as a hero. But when Aegeus saw his valour, he envied him, and feared lest he should join the sons of Pallas, and take away the sceptre from him. So he plotted against his life, and slew him basely, no man knows how or where. Some say that he waylaid him by Oinoe, on the road which goes to Thebes, and some that he sent him against the bull of Marathon, that the beast might kill him. But Aegeus says that the young men killed him from envy, because he had conquered them in the games. So Minos came hither and avenged him, and would not depart till this land had promised him tribute—seven youths and seven maidens every year, who go with me in a black-sailed ship, till they come to hundred-citied Crete.'

And Theseus ground his teeth together, and said: 'Wert thou not a herald I would kill thee for saying such things of my father; but I will go to him, and know the truth.' So he went to his father, and asked him, but he turned away his head and wept, and said: 'Blood was shed in the land unjustly, and by blood it is avenged. Break not my heart by question; it is enough to endure in silence.'

Then Theseus groaned inwardly, and said: 'I will go myself with these youths and maidens, and kill Minos upon his royal throne.'

And Aegeus shrieked and cried: 'You shall not go, my son, the light of my old age, to whom alone I look to rule this people after I am dead and gone. You shall not go, to die horribly, as those youths and maidens die; for Minos thrusts them into a labyrinth, which Daidalos made for him among the rocks—Daidalos the renegade, the accursed, the pest of this his native land. From that labyrinth no one can escape, entangled in its winding ways, before they meet the Minotaur, the monster who feeds upon the flesh of men. There he devours them horribly, and they never see this land again.'

Then Theseus grew red and his ears tingled and his heart beat loud in his bosom. And he stood awhile like a tall stone pillar on the cliffs above some hero's grave, and at last he spoke:

'Therefore all the more I will go with them, and slay the accursed beast. Have I not slain all evil-doers and monsters, that I might free this land? Where are Periphetes, and Sinis and Kerkyon and Phaia the wild sow? Where are the fifty sons of Pallas? And this Minotaur shall go the road which they have gone, and Minos himself, if he dare stay me.'

'But how will you slay him, my son? For you must leave your club and your armour behind, and be cast to the monster, defenceless and naked like the rest.'

And Theseus said: 'Are there no stones in that labyrinth; and have I not fists and teeth? Did I need my club to kill Kerkyon, the terror of all mortal men?'

Then Aegeus clung to his knees, but he would not hear; and at last he let him go, weeping bitterly, and said only this one word:

'Promise me but this, if you return in peace, though that may hardly be: take down the black sail of the ship (for I shall watch for it all day upon the cliffs) and hoist instead a white sail; that I may know afar off that you are safe.'

And Theseus promised and went out and to the market-place where the herald stood, while they drew lots for the youths and maidens, who were to sail in that doleful crew. And the people stood wailing and weeping, as the lot fell on this one and on that; but Theseus strode into the midst, and cried:

'Here is a youth who needs no lot. I myself will be one of the seven.'

And the herald asked in wonder: 'Fair youth, know you whither you are going?'

And Theseus said: 'I know. Let us go down to the black-sailed ship.'

So they went down to the black-sailed ship, seven maidens and seven youths and Theseus before them all, and the people following them lamenting. But Theseus whispered to his companions: 'Have hope, for the monster is not immortal. Where are Periphetes and Sinis and Sciron and all whom I have slain?' Then their hearts were comforted a little, but they wept as they went on board, and the cliffs of Sunium rang, and all the isles of the Aegean Sea with the voice of their lamentation, as they sailed on towards their deaths in Crete.

★   ★   ★   ★

And at last they came to Crete, and to Cnossus, beneath the peaks of Ida, and to the palace of Minos, the great king, to whom Zeus himself taught laws. So he was the wisest of all mortal kings, and conquered all the Aegean isles, and his ships were as many as the sea-gulls, and his palace like a marble hill. And he sat among the pillars of the hall, upon his throne of beaten gold, and around him stood the speaking statues which Daidalos had made by his skill. For Daidalos was the most cunning of all Athenians, and he invented the plumb-line and the auger and glue, and many a tool with which wood is wrought. And he first set up masts in ships, and yards, and his son made sails for them; but Perdix his nephew excelled him, for he invented the saw and its teeth, copying it from the backbone of a fish, and invented, too, the chisel and the compasses, and the potter's wheel which moulds the clay. Therefore Daidalos envied him, and hurled him headlong from the temple of Athené; but the goddess pitied him (for she loves the wise) and changed him into a partridge, which flits for ever about the hills. And Daidalos fled to Crete, to Minos, and worked for him many a year, till he did a shameful deed, at which the sun hid his face on high.

Then he fled from the anger of Minos, he and Icaros his son having made themselves wings of feathers, and fixed the feathers with wax. So they flew over the sea towards Sicily; but Icaros flew too near the sun; and the wax of his wings was melted, and he fell into the Icarian Sea. But Daidalos came safe to Sicily, and there wrought many a wondrous work, for he made for King Cocalos a reservoir, from which a great river watered all the land, and a castle and a treasury on a mountain, which the giants themselves could not have stormed. And in Selinos he took the steam which comes up from the fires of Aetna, and made of it a warm bath of vapour, to cure the pains of mortal men, and he made a honeycomb of gold, in which the bees came and stored their honey, and in Egypt he made the forecourt of the temple of Hephaistos in Memphis, and a statue of himself within it, and many another wondrous work. And for Minos he made statues which spoke and moved, and the temple of Britomartis, and the dancing-hall of Ariadne, which he carved of fair white stone. And in Sardinia he worked for Iölaos, and in many a land beside, wandering up and down for ever with his cunning, unlovely and accursed by men.

But Theseus stood before Minos, and they looked each other in the face. And Minos bade take them to prison, and cast them to the monster one by one, that the death of Androgeos might be avenged. Then Theseus cried:

'A boon, O Minos! Let me be thrown first to the beast. For I came hither for that very purpose of my own will, and not by lot.'

'Who art thou, then, brave youth?'

'I am the son of him whom of all men thou hatest most—Aegeus the King of Athens; and I am come here to end this matter.'

And Minos pondered awhile, looking steadfastly at him, and he thought: 'The lad means to atone by his own death for his father's sin'; and he answered at last mildly:

'Go back in peace, my son. It is a pity that one so brave should die.'

But Theseus said: 'I have sworn that I will not go back till I have seen the monster face to face.'

And at that Minos frowned, and said: 'Then thou shalt see him; take the madman away.'

And they led Theseus away into the prison, with the other youths and maids.

But Ariadne, Minos' daughter, saw him, as she came out of her white stone hall; and she loved him for his courage and his majesty, and said: 'Shame that such a youth should die!' And by night she went down to the prison, and told him all her heart, and said:

'Flee down to your ship at once, for I have bribed the guards before the door. Flee, you and all your friends, and go back in peace to Greece, and take me, take me with you! For I dare not stay after you are gone, for my father will kill me miserably, if he knows what I have done.'

And Theseus stood silent awhile, for he was astonished and confounded by her beauty; but at last he said: 'I cannot go home in peace, till I have seen and slain this Minotaur, and avenged the deaths of the youths and maidens and put an end to the terrors of my land.'

'And will you kill the Minotaur? How, then?'

'I know not, nor do I care: but he must be strong, if he be too strong for me.'

Then she loved him all the more, and said:

'But when you have killed him, how will you find your way out of the labyrinth?'

'I know not, neither do I care: but it must be a strange road, if I do not find it out before I have eaten up the monster's carcass.'

Then she loved him all the more, and said:

'Fair youth, you are too bold; but I can help you, weak as I am. I will give you a sword, and with that perhaps you may slay the beast; and a clue of thread, and by that, perhaps, you may find your way out again. Only promise me that if you escape safe you will take me home with you to Greece, for my father will surely kill me, if he knows what I have done.'

Then Theseus laughed and said: 'Am I not safe enough now?' And he hid the sword in his bosom, and rolled up the clue in his hand, and then he swore to Ariadne, and fell down before her and kissed her hands and her feet, and she wept over him a long while, and then went away; and Theseus lay down and slept sweetly.

And when the evening came, the guards came in and led him away to the labyrinth.

And he went down into that doleful gulf, through winding paths among the rocks, under caverns and arches and galleries and over heaps of fallen stone. And he turned on the left hand and on the right hand, and went up and down, till his head was dizzy; but all the while he held his clue. For when he went in he had fastened it to a stone, and left it to unroll out of his hand as he went on; and it lasted him till he met the Minotaur, in a narrow chasm between black cliffs.

And when he saw him he stopped awhile, for he had never seen so strange a beast. His body was a man's; but his head was the head of a bull, and his teeth were the teeth of a lion, and with them he tore his prey. And when he saw Theseus he roared, and put his head down, and rushed right at him.

But Theseus stept aside nimbly, and as he passed by, cut him in the

The unnatural beast bellowed and charged at Theseus.

knee; and ere he could turn in the narrow path, he followed him, and stabbed him again and again from behind, till the monster fled bellowing wildly; for never before had he felt a wound. And Theseus followed him at full speed, holding the clue of thread in his left hand.

Then on, through cavern after cavern, under dark ribs of sounding stone, and up rough glens and torrent beds, among the sunless roots of Ida, and to the edge of the eternal snow, went they, the hunter and the hunted, while the hills bellowed to the monster's bellow.

And at last Theseus came up with him, where he lay panting on a slab among the snow, and caught him by the horns, and forced his head back and drove the keen sword through his throat.

Then he turned, and went back limping and weary, feeling his way down by the clue of thread, till he came to the mouth of that doleful place; and saw waiting for him—whom but Ariadne!

And he whispered: 'It is done!' and showed her the sword; and she laid her finger on her lips and led him to the prison, and opened the doors, and set all the prisoners free, while the guards lay sleeping heavily, for she had silenced them with wine.

Then they fled to their ship together and leapt on board and hoisted up the sail; and the night lay dark around them, so that they passed through Minos' ships and escaped all safe to Naxos; and there Ariadne became Theseus' wife.

THE WHITE SEAL

Rudyard Kipling

Oh! hush thee, my baby, the night is behind us,
And black are the waters that sparkled so green.
The moon, o'er the combers, looks downward to find us
At rest in the hollows that rustle between.
Where billow meets billow, there soft be thy pillow;
Ah, weary wee flipperling, curl at thy ease!
The storm shall not wake thee, nor shark overtake thee,
Asleep in the arms of the slow-swinging seas.

Seal Lullaby

All these things happened several years ago at a place called Novastoshnah, or North East Point, on the Island of St Paul, away and away in the Bering Sea. Limmershin, the Winter Wren, told me the tale when he was blown on to the rigging of a steamer going to Japan, and I took him down into my cabin and warmed and fed him for a couple of days till he was fit to fly back to St Paul's again. Limmershin is a very odd little bird, but he knows how to tell the truth.

Nobody comes to Novastoshnah except on business, and the only people who have regular business there are the seals. They come in the summer months by hundreds and hundreds of thousands out of the cold grey sea; for Novastoshnah Beach has the finest accommodation for seals of any place in all the world.

Sea Catch knew that, and every spring would swim from whatever place he happened to be in—would swim like a torpedo-boat straight for Novastoshnah, and spend a month fighting with his companions for a good place on the rocks as close to the sea as possible. Sea Catch was fifteen years old, a huge grey fur-seal with almost a mane on his shoulders, and long, wicked dog-teeth. When he heaved himself up on his front flippers he stood more than four feet clear of the ground, and his weight, if any one had been bold enough to weigh him, was nearly seven hundred pounds. He was scarred all over with the marks of savage fights, but he was always ready for just one fight more. He would put his head on one side, as though he were afraid to look his enemy in the face; then he would shoot it out like lightning, and when the big teeth were firmly fixed on the other seal's neck, the other seal might get away if he could, but Sea Catch would not help him.

Yet Sea Catch never chased a beaten seal, for that was against the Rules of the Beach. He only wanted room by the sea for his nursery; but as there were forty or fifty thousand other seals hunting for the same thing each spring, the whistling, bellowing, roaring, and blowing on the beach were something frightful.

From a little hill called Hutchinson's Hill you could look over three and a half miles of ground covered with fighting seals; and the surf was dotted all over with the heads of seals hurrying to land and begin their share of the fighting. They fought in the breakers, they fought in the sand, and they fought on the smooth-worn basalt rocks of the nurseries; for they were just as stupid and unaccommodating as men. Their wives never came to the island until late in May or early in June, for they did not care to be torn to pieces; and the young two-, three-, and four-year-old seals who had not begun housekeeping went inland about half a mile through the ranks of the fighters and played about on the sand-dunes in droves and legions, and rubbed off every single green thing that grew. They were called the holluschickie,—the bachelors,—and there were perhaps two or three hundred thousand of them at Novastoshnah alone.

Sea Catch had just finished his forty-fifth fight one spring when Matkah, his soft, sleek, gentle-eyed wife, came up out of the sea, and he caught her by the scruff of the neck and dumped her down on his reservation, saying gruffly: 'Late, as usual. Where *have* you been?'

It was not the fashion for Sea Catch to eat anything during the four months he stayed on the beaches, and so his temper was generally bad. Matkah knew better than to answer back. She looked round and cooed: 'How thoughtful of you! You've taken the old place again.'

'I should think I had,' said Sea Catch. 'Look at me!'

He was scratched and bleeding in twenty places; one eye was almost blind, and his sides were torn to ribbons.

'Oh, you men, you men!' Matkah said, fanning herself with her hind flipper. 'Why can't you be sensible and settle your places quietly? You look as though you had been fighting with the Killer Whale.'

'I haven't been doing anything *but* fight since the middle of May. The beach is disgracefully crowded this season. I've met at least a hundred seals from Lukannon Beach, house-hunting. Why can't people stay where they belong?'

'I've often thought we should be much happier if we hauled out at Otter Island instead of this crowded place,' said Matkah.

'Bah! Only the holluschickie go to Otter Island. If we went there they would say we were afraid. We must preserve appearances, my dear.'

Sea Catch sunk his head proudly between his fat shoulders and pretended to go to sleep for a few minutes, but all the time he was keeping a sharp look-out for a fight. Now that all the seals and their wives were on the land, you could hear their clamour miles out to sea above the loudest gales. At the lowest counting there were over a million seals on the beach,—old seals, mother seals, tiny babies, and holluschickie, fighting, scuffling, bleating, crawling, and playing together,—going down to the sea and coming up from it in gangs and regiments, lying over every foot of ground as far as the eye could reach, and skirmishing about in brigades through the fog. It is nearly always foggy at Novastoshnah, except when the sun comes out and makes everything look all pearly and rainbow-coloured for a little while.

Kotick, Matkah's baby, was born in the middle of that confusion, and he was all head and shoulders, with pale, watery-blue eyes, as tiny seals must be; but there was something about his coat that made his mother look at him very closely.

'Sea Catch,' she said at last, 'our baby's going to be white!'

'Empty clam-shells and dry seaweed!' snorted Sea Catch. 'There never has been such a thing in the world as a white seal.'

'I can't help that,' said Matkah; 'there's going to be now'; and she sang the low, crooning seal-song that all the mother seals sing to their babies:

> You mustn't swim till you're six weeks old,
> Or your head will be sunk by your heels;
> And summer gales and Killer Whales
> Are bad for baby seals.
>
> Are bad for baby seals, dear rat,
> As bad as bad can be;
> But splash and grow strong,
> And you can't be wrong,
> Child of the Open Sea!

Of course the little fellow did not understand the words at first. He paddled and scrambled about by his mother's side, and learned to scuffle out of the way when his father was fighting with another seal, and the two rolled and roared up and down the slippery rocks. Matkah used to go to sea to get things to eat, and the baby was fed only once in two days; but then he ate all he could, and throve upon it.

The first thing he did was to crawl inland, and there he met tens of thousands of babies of his own age, and they played together like puppies, went to sleep on the clean sand, and played again. The old people in the nurseries took no notice of them, and the holluschickie kept to their own grounds, so the babies had a beautiful playtime.

When Matkah came back from her deep-sea fishing she would go straight to their playground and call as a sheep calls for a lamb, and wait until she heard Kotick bleat. Then she would take the straightest of straight lines in his direction, striking out with her fore flippers and knocking the youngsters head over heels right and left. There were always a few hundred mothers hunting for their children through the playgrounds, and the babies were kept lively; but, as Matkah told Kotick, 'So long as you don't lie in muddy water and get mange, or rub the hard sand into a cut or scratch, and so long as you never go swimming when there is a heavy sea, nothing will hurt you here.'

Little seals can no more swim than little children, but they are unhappy till they learn. The first time that Kotick went down to the sea a wave carried him out beyond his depth, and his big head sank and his little hind flippers flew up exactly as his mother had told him in the song, and if the next wave had not thrown him back again he would have drowned.

After that he learned to lie in a beach-pool and let the wash of the waves just cover him and lift him up while he paddled, but he always kept his eye open for big waves that might hurt. He was two weeks learning to use his flippers; and all that while he floundered in and out of the water, and coughed and grunted and crawled up the beach and took cat-naps on the sand, and went back again, until at last he found that he truly belonged to the water.

Then you can imagine the times that he had with his companions, ducking under the rollers; or coming in on top of a comber and landing with a swash and a splutter as the big wave went whirling far up the beach; or standing up on his tail and scratching his head as the old people did; or playing 'I'm the King of the Castle' on slippery, weedy rocks that just stuck out of the wash. Now and then he would see a thin fin, like a big shark's fin, drifting along close to the shore, and he knew that that was the Killer Whale, the Grampus, who eats young seals when he can get them; and Kotick would head for the beach like an arrow, and the fin would jig off slowly, as if it were looking for nothing at all.

Late in October the seals began to leave St Paul's for the deep sea, by families and tribes, and there was no more fighting over the nurseries, and the holluschickie played anywhere they liked. 'Next year,' said Matkah to Kotick, 'you will be a holluschickie; but this year you must learn how to catch fish.'

They set out together across the Pacific, and Matkah showed Kotick how to sleep on his back with his flippers tucked down by his side and his little nose just out of the water. No cradle is so comfortable as the long, rocking swell of the Pacific. When Kotick felt his skin tingle all over, Matkah told him he was learning the 'feel of the water', and that tingly, prickly feelings meant bad weather coming, and he must swim hard and get away.

'In a little time,' she said, 'you'll know where to swim to, but just now we'll follow Sea Pig, the Porpoise, for he is very wise.' A school of porpoises were ducking and tearing through the water, and little Kotick followed them as fast as he could. 'How do you know where to go to?' he panted. The leader of the school rolled his white eyes, and ducked under. 'My tail tingles, youngster,' he said. 'That means there's a gale behind me. Come along! When you're south of the Sticky Water [he meant the Equator], and your tail tingles, that means there's a gale in front of you and you must head north. Come along! The water feels bad here.'

This was one of the very many things that Kotick learned, and he was always learning. Matkah taught him to follow the cod and the halibut along the undersea banks, and wrench the rockling out of his hole among the weeds; how to skirt the wrecks lying a hundred fathoms below water, and dart like a rifle-bullet in at one port-hole and out at another as the fishes ran; how to dance on the top of the waves when the lightning was racing all over the sky, and wave his flipper politely to the stumpy-tailed Albatross and the Man-of-War Hawk as they went down the wind; how to jump three or four feet clear of the water, like a dolphin, flippers close to the side and tail curved; to leave the flying-fish alone because they are all bony; to take the shoulder-piece out of a cod at full speed ten fathoms deep; and never to stop and look at a boat or a ship, but particularly a row-boat. At the end of six months, what Kotick did not know about deep-sea fishing was not worth knowing, and all that time he never set flipper on dry ground.

One day, however, as he was lying half asleep in the warm water somewhere off the Island of Juan Fernandez, he felt faint and lazy all over, just as human people do when the spring is in their legs, and he remembered the good firm beaches of Novastoshnah seven thousand miles away, the games his companions played, the smell of the sea-weed, the seal roar, and the fighting. That very minute he turned north, swimming steadily, and as he went on he met scores of his mates, all bound for the same place, and they said: 'Greeting, Kotick! This year we are all holluschickie, and we can dance the Fire-dance in the breakers off Lukannon and play on the new grass. But where did you get that coat?'

Kotick's fur was almost pure white now, and though he felt very proud of it, he only said: 'Swim quickly! My bones are aching for the land.' And so they all came to the beaches where they had been born, and heard the old seals, their fathers, fighting in the rolling mist.

That night Kotick danced the Fire-dance with the yearling seals. The sea is full of fire on summer nights all the way down from Novastoshnah to Lukannon, and each seal leaves a wake like burning oil behind him, and a flaming flash when he jumps, and the waves break in great phosphorescent streaks and swirls. Then they went inland to the holluschickie grounds, and rolled up and down in the new wild wheat, and told stories of what they had done while they had been at sea. They talked about the Pacific as boys would talk about a wood that they had been nutting in, and if any one had understood them, he could have gone away and made such a chart of that ocean as never was. The three- and four-year-old holluschickie romped down from Hutchinson's Hill, crying: 'Out of the way, youngsters! The sea is deep, and you don't know all that's in it yet. Wait till you've rounded the Horn. Hi, you yearling, where did you get that white coat?'

'I didn't get it,' said Kotick; 'it grew.' And just as he was going to roll the speaker over, a couple of black-haired men with flat red faces came from behind a sand-dune, and Kotick, who had never seen a man before, coughed and lowered his head. The holluschickie just bundled off a few yards and sat staring stupidly. The men were no less than Kerick Booterin, the chief of the seal-hunters on the island, and Patalamon, his son. They came from the little village not half a mile from the seal-nurseries, and they were deciding what seals they would drive up to the killing-pens (for the seals were driven just like sheep), to be turned into sealskin jackets later on.

'Ho!' said Patalamon. 'Look! There's a white seal!'

Kerick Booterin turned nearly white under his oil and smoke, for he was an Aleut, and Aleuts are not clean people. Then he began to mutter a prayer. 'Don't touch him, Patalamon. There has never been a white seal since—since I was born. Perhaps it is old Zaharrof's ghost. He was lost last year in the big gale.'

'I'm not going near him,' said Patalamon. 'He's unlucky. Do you really think he is old Zaharrof come back? I owe him for some gulls' eggs.'

Kotick returned triumphantly to tell them of his miraculous find.

'Don't look at him,' said Kerick. 'Head off that drove of four-year-olds. The men ought to skin two hundred today, but it's the beginning of the season, and they are new to the work. A hundred will do. Quick!'

Patalamon rattled a pair of seal's shoulder-bones in front of a herd of holluschickie, and they stopped dead, puffing and blowing. Then he stepped near, and the seals began to move, and Kerick headed them inland, and they never tried to get back to their companions. Hundreds and hundreds of thousands of seals watched them being driven, but they went on playing just the same. Kotick was the only one who asked questions, and none of his companions could tell him anything, except that the men always drove seals in that way for six weeks or two months of every year.

'I am going to follow,' he said, and his eyes nearly popped out of his head as he shuffled along in the wake of the herd.

'The white seal is coming after us,' cried Patalamon. 'That's the first time a seal has ever come to the killing-grounds alone.'

'Hsh! Don't look behind you,' said Kerick. 'It *is* Zaharrof's ghost! I must speak to the priest about this.'

The distance to the killing-grounds was only half a mile, but it took an hour to cover, because if the seals went too fast Kerick knew that they would get heated and then their fur would come off in patches when they were skinned. So they went on very slowly, past Sea-Lion's Neck, past Webster House, till they came to the Salt House just beyond the sight of the seals on the beach. Kotick followed, panting and wondering. He thought that he was at the world's end, but the roar of the seal-nurseries behind him sounded as loud as the roar of a train in a tunnel. Then Kerick sat down on the moss and pulled out a heavy pewter watch and let the drove cool off for thirty minutes, and Kotick could hear the fog-dew dripping from the brim of his cap. Then ten or twelve men, each with an iron-bound club three or four feet long, came up, and Kerick pointed out one or two of the drove that were bitten by their companions or were too hot, and the men kicked those aside with their heavy boots made of the skin of a walrus's throat, and then Kerick said: 'Let's go!' and then the men clubbed the seals on the head as fast as they could.

Ten minutes later little Kotick did not recognize his friends any more, for their skins were ripped off from the nose to the hind flippers—whipped off and thrown down on the ground in a pile.

That was enough for Kotick. He turned and galloped (a seal can gallop very swiftly for a short time) back to the sea, his little new moustache bristling with horror. At Sea-Lion's Neck, where the great sea-lions sit on the edge of the surf, he flung himself flipper over head into the cool water, and rocked there, gasping miserably. 'What's here?' said a sea-lion gruffly; for as a rule the sea-lions keep themselves to themselves.

'*Scoochnie! Ochen scoochnie!*' ('I'm lonesome, very lonesome!') said Kotick. 'They're killing *all* the holluschickie on *all* the beaches!'

The sea-lion turned his head inshore. 'Nonsense!' he said; 'your friends are making as much noise as ever. You must have seen old Kerick polishing off a drove. He's done that for thirty years.'

'It's horrible,' said Kotick, backing water as a wave went over him, and steadying himself with a screw-stroke of his flippers that brought him up all standing within three inches of a jagged edge of rock.

'Well done for a yearling!' said the sea-lion, who could appreciate good swimming. 'I suppose it *is* rather awful from your way of looking at it; but if you seals will come here year after year, of course the men get to know of it, and unless you can find an island where no men ever come, you will always be driven.'

'Isn't there any such island?' began Kotick.

'I've followed the *poltoos* [the halibut] for twenty years, and I can't say I've found it yet. But look here—you seem to have a fondness for talking to your betters; suppose you go to Walrus Islet and talk to Sea Vitch. He may know something. Don't flounce off like that. It's a six-mile swim, and if I were you I should haul out and take a nap first, little one.'

Kotick thought that that was good advice, so he swam round to his own beach, hauled out, and slept for half an hour, twitching all over, as seals will. Then he headed straight for Walrus Islet, a little low sheet of rocky island almost due north-east from Novastoshnah, all ledges of rock and gulls' nests, where the walrus herded by themselves.

He landed close to old Sea Vitch—the big, ugly, bloated, pimpled, fat-necked, long-tusked walrus of the North Pacific, who has no manners except when he is asleep—as he was then, with his hind flippers half in and half out of the surf.

'Wake up!' barked Kotick, for the gulls were making a great noise.

'Hah! Ho! Hmph! What's that?' said Sea Vitch, and he struck the next walrus a blow with his tusks and waked him up, and the next struck the next, and so on till they were all awake and staring in every direction but the right one.

'Hi! It's me,' said Kotick, bobbing in the surf and looking like a little white slug.

'Well! May I be—skinned!' said Sea Vitch, and they all looked at Kotick as you can fancy a club full of drowsy old gentlemen would look at a little boy. Kotick did not care to hear any more about skinning just then; he had seen enough of it; so he called out: 'Isn't there any place for seals to go where men don't ever come?'

'Go and find out,' said Sea Vitch, shutting his eyes. 'Run away. We're busy here.'

Kotick made his dolphin-jump in the air and shouted as loud as he could: 'Clam-eater! Clam-eater!' He knew that Sea Vitch never caught a fish in his life, but always rooted for clams and seaweeds, though he pretended to be a very terrible person. Naturally the Chickies and the Gooverooskies and the Epatkas, the Burgomaster Gulls and the Kittiwakes and the Puffins, who are always looking for a chance to be rude, took up the cry, and—so Limmershin told me—for nearly five minutes you could not have heard a gun fired on Walrus Islet. All the population was yelling and screaming: 'Clam-eater! *Stareek* [old man]!' while Sea Vitch rolled from side to side grunting and coughing.

'*Now* will you tell?' said Kotick, all out of breath.

'Go and ask Sea Cow,' said Sea Vitch. 'If he is living still, he'll be able to tell you.'

'How shall I know Sea Cow when I meet him?' said Kotick, sheering off.

'He's the only thing in the sea uglier than Sea Vitch,' screamed a Burgomaster Gull, wheeling under Sea Vitch's nose. 'Uglier, and with worse manners! *Stareek!*'

Kotick swam back to Novastoshnah, leaving the gulls to scream. There he found that no one sympathized with him in his little attempts to discover a quiet place for the seals. They told him that men had always driven the holluschickie—it was part of the day's work—and that if he did not like to see ugly things he should not have gone to the killing-grounds. But none of the other seals had seen the killing, and that made the difference between him and his friends. Besides, Kotick was a white seal.

'What you must do,' said old Sea Catch, after he had heard his son's adventures, 'is to grow up and be a big seal like your father, and have a nursery on the beach, and then they will leave you alone. In another five years you ought to be able to fight for yourself.' Even gentle Matkah, his mother, said: 'You will never be able to stop the killing. Go and play in the sea, Kotick.' And Kotick went off and danced the Fire-dance with a very heavy little heart.

That autumn he left the beach as soon as he could, and set off alone because of a notion in his bullet-head. He was going to find Sea Cow, if there was such a person in the sea, and he was going to find a quiet island with good firm beaches for seals to live on, where men could not get at them. So he explored and explored by himself from the North to the South Pacific, swimming as much as three hundred miles in a day and night. He met with more adventures than can be told, and narrowly escaped being caught by the Basking Shark, and the Spotted Shark, and the Hammerhead, and he met all the untrustworthy ruffians that loaf up and down the seas, and the heavy polite fish, and the scarlet-spotted scallops that are moored in one place for hundreds of years, and grow very proud of it; but he never met Sea Cow, and he never found an island that he could fancy.

If the beach was good and hard, with a slope behind it for seals to play on, there was always the smoke of a whaler on the horizon, boiling down blubber, and Kotick knew what *that* meant. Or else he could see that seals had once visited the island and been killed off, and Kotick knew that where men had come once they would come again.

He picked up with an old stumpy-tailed albatross, who told him that Kerguelen Island was the very place for peace and quiet, and when Kotick went down there he was all but smashed to pieces against some wicked black cliffs in a heavy sleet-storm with lightning and thunder. Yet as he pulled out against the gale he could see that even there had once been a seal-nursery. And so it was in all the other islands that he visited.

Limmershin gave a long list of them, for he said that Kotick spent five seasons exploring, with a four months' rest each year at Novastoshnah, when the holluschickie used to make fun of him and his imaginary islands. He went to the Galapagos, a horrid dry place on the Equator, where he was nearly baked to death; he went to the Georgia Islands, the South Orkneys, Emerald Island, Little Nightingale Island, Gough's Island, Bouvet's Island, the Crossets, and even to a little speck of an island south of the Cape of Good Hope. But everywhere the People of the Sea told him the same things. Seals had come to those islands once upon a time, but men had killed them all off. Even when he swam thousands of miles out of the Pacific, and got to a place called Cape Corrientes (that was when he was coming back from Gough's Island), he found a few hundred mangy seals on a rock, and they told him that men came there too.

That nearly broke his heart, and he headed round the Horn back to his own beaches; and on his way north he hauled out on an island full of green trees, where he found an old, old seal who was dying, and Kotick caught fish for him, and told him all his sorrows. 'Now,' said Kotick, 'I am going back to Novastoshnah, and if I am driven to the killing-pens with the holluschickie I shall not care.'

The old seal said: 'Try once more. I am the last of the Lost Rookery of Masafuera, and in the days when men killed us by the hundred thousand there was a story on the beaches that some day a white seal would come out of the north and lead the seal people to a quiet place. I am old and I shall never live to see that day, but others will. Try once more.'

And Kotick curled up his moustache (it was a beauty), and said: 'I am the only white seal that has ever been born on the beaches, and I am the only seal, black or white, who ever thought of looking for new islands.'

That cheered him immensely; and when he came back to Novastoshnah that summer, Matkah, his mother, begged him to marry and settle down, for he was no longer a holluschick, but a full-grown sea-catch, with a curly white mane on his shoulders as heavy, as big, and as fierce as his father. 'Give me another season,' he said.

'Remember, Mother, it is always the seventh wave that goes farthest up the beach.'

Curiously enough, there was another seal who thought that she would put off marrying till the next year, and Kotick danced the Fire-dance with her all down Lukannon Beach the night before he set off on his last exploration.

This time he went westward, because he had fallen on the trail of a great shoal of halibut, and he needed at least one hundred pounds of fish a day to keep him in good condition. He chased them till he was tired, and then he curled himself up and went to sleep on the hollows of the ground-swell that sets in to Copper Island. He knew the coast perfectly well, so about midnight, when he felt himself gently bumped on a weed-bed, he said, 'H'm, tide's running strong tonight,' and turning over under water opened his eyes slowly and stretched. Then he jumped like a cat, for he saw huge things nosing about in the shoal water and browsing on the heavy fringes of the weeds.

'By the Great Combers of Magellan!' he said, beneath his moustache. 'Who in the Deep Sea are these people?'

They were like no walrus, sea-lion, seal, bear, whale, shark, fish, squid, or scallop that Kotick had ever seen before. They were between twenty and thirty feet long, and they had no hind flippers, but a shovel-like tail that looked as if it had been whittled out of wet leather. Their heads were the most foolish-looking things you ever saw, and they balanced on the ends of their tails in deep water when they weren't grazing, bowing solemnly to one another and waving their front flippers as a fat man waves his arm.

'Ahem!' said Kotick. 'Good sport, gentlemen?' The big things answered by bowing and waving their flippers like the Frog-Footman. When they began feeding again Kotick saw that their upper lip was split into two pieces that they could twitch apart about a foot and bring together again with a whole bushel of seaweed between the splits. They tucked the stuff into their mouths and chumped solemnly.

'Messy style of feeding, that,' said Kotick. They bowed again, and Kotick began to lose his temper. 'Very good,' he said. 'If you do happen to have an extra joint in your front flipper you needn't show off so. I see you bow gracefully, but I should like to know your names.'

The split lips moved and twitched, and the glassy green eyes stared; but they did not speak.

'Well!' said Kotick, 'you're the only people I've ever met uglier than Sea Vitch—and with worse manners.'

Then he remembered in a flash what the Burgomaster Gull had screamed to him when he was a little yearling at Walrus Islet, and he tumbled backward in the water, for he knew that he had found Sea Cow at last.

The sea cows went on schlooping and grazing and chumping in the weed, and Kotick asked them questions in every language that he had picked up in his travels: and the Sea People talk nearly as many languages as human beings. But the Sea Cow did not answer, because Sea Cow cannot talk. He has only six bones in his neck where he ought to have seven, and they say under the sea that that prevents him from speaking even to his companions; but, as you know, he has an extra joint in his fore flipper, and by waving it up and down and about he makes a sort of clumsy telegraphic code.

By daylight Kotick's mane was standing on end and his temper was gone where the dead crabs go. Then the Sea Cow began to travel northward very slowly, stopping to hold absurd bowing councils from time to time, and Kotick followed them, saying to himself: 'People who are such idiots as these are would have been killed long ago if they hadn't found out some safe island; and what is good enough for the Sea Cow is good enough for the Sea Catch. All the same, I wish they'd hurry.'

It was weary work for Kotick. The herd never went more than forty or fifty miles a day, and stopped to feed at night, and kept close to the shore all the time; while Kotick swam round them, and over them, and under them, but he could not hurry them on one half-mile. As they went farther north they held a bowing council every few hours, and Kotick nearly bit off his moustache with impatience till he saw that they were following up a warm current of water, and then he respected them more.

One night they sank through the shiny water—sank like stones—and, for the first time since he had known them, began to swim quickly. Kotick followed, and the pace astonished him, for he never dreamed that Sea Cow was anything of a swimmer. They headed for a cliff by the shore—a cliff that ran down into deep water, and plunged into a dark hole at the foot of it, twenty fathoms under the sea. It was a long, long swim, and Kotick badly wanted fresh air before he was out of the dark tunnel that they led him through.

'My wig!' he said, when he rose, gasping and puffing, into open water at the farther end. 'It was a long dive, but it was worth it.'

The sea cows had separated, and were browsing lazily along the edges of the finest beaches that Kotick had ever seen. There were long stretches of smooth-worn rock running for miles, exactly fitted to make seal-nurseries, and there were playgrounds of hard sand sloping inland behind them, and there were rollers for seals to dance in, and long grass to roll in, and sand-dunes to climb up and down; and, best of all, Kotick knew by the feel of the water, which never deceives a true Sea Catch, that no men had ever come there.

The first thing he did was to assure himself that the fishing was good, and then he swam along the beaches and counted up the delightful low sandy islands half hidden in the beautiful rolling fog. Away to the northward out to sea ran a line of bars and shoals and rocks that would never let a ship come within six miles of the beach; and between the islands and the mainland was a stretch of deep water that ran up to the perpendicular cliffs, and somewhere below the cliffs was the mouth of the tunnel.

'It's Novastoshnah over again, but ten times better,' said Kotick. 'Sea Cow must be wiser than I thought. Men can't come down the cliffs, even if there were any men; and the shoals to seaward would knock a ship to splinters. If any place in the sea is safe, this is it.'

He began to think of the seal he had left behind him, but though he was in a hurry to go back to Novastoshnah, he thoroughly explored the new country, so that he would be able to answer all questions.

Then he dived and made sure of the mouth of the tunnel, and raced through to the southward. No one but a sea cow or a seal would have dreamed of there being such a place, and when he looked back at the cliffs even Kotick could hardly believe that he had been under them.

He was six days going home, though he was not swimming slowly; and when he hauled out just above Sea-Lion's Neck the first person he met was the seal who had been waiting for him, and she saw by the look in his eyes that he had found his island at last.

But the holluschickie and Sea Catch, his father, and all the other seals, laughed at him when he told them what he had discovered, and a young seal about his own age said: 'This is all very well, Kotick, but you can't come from no one knows where and order us off like this. Remember we've been fighting for our nurseries, and that's a thing you never did. You preferred prowling about in the sea.'

The other seals laughed at this, and the young seal began twisting his head from side to side. He had just married that year, and was making a great fuss about it.

'I've no nursery to fight for,' said Kotick. 'I want only to show you all a place where you will be safe. What's the use of fighting?'

'Oh, if you're trying to back out, of course I've no more to say,' said the young seal, with an ugly chuckle.

'Will you come with me if I win?' said Kotick; and a green light came into his eyes, for he was very angry at having to fight at all.

'Very good,' said the young seal carelessly. '*If* you win, I'll come.'

He had no time to change his mind, for Kotick's head darted out and his teeth sank in the blubber of the young seal's neck. Then he threw himself back on his haunches and hauled his enemy down the beach, shook him, and knocked him over. Then Kotick roared to the seals: 'I've done my best for you these five seasons past. I've found you the island where you'll be safe, but unless your heads are dragged off your silly necks you won't believe. I'm going to teach you now. Look out for yourselves!'

Limmershin told me that never in his life—and Limmershin sees ten thousand big seals fighting every year—never in all his little life did he see anything like Kotick's charge into the nurseries. He flung himself at the biggest sea-catch he could find, caught him by the throat, choked him and bumped him and banged him till he grunted for mercy, and then threw him aside and attacked the next. You see, Kotick had never fasted for four months as the big seals did every year, and his deep-sea swimming-trips kept him in perfect condition, and, best of all, he had never fought before. His curly white mane stood up with rage, and his eyes flamed, and his big dog-teeth glistened, and he was splendid to look at.

Old Sea Catch, his father, saw him tearing past, hauling the grizzled old seals about as though they had been halibut, and upsetting the young bachelors in all directions; and Sea Catch gave one roar and shouted: 'He may be a fool, but he is the best fighter on the Beaches. Don't tackle your father, my son! He's with you!'

Kotick roared in answer, and old Sea Catch waddled in, his moustache on end, blowing like a locomotive, while Matkah and the seal that was going to marry Kotick cowered down and admired their men-folk. It was a gorgeous fight, for the two fought as long as there was a seal that dared lift up his head, and then they paraded grandly up and down the beach side by side, bellowing.

At night, just as the Northern Lights were winking and flashing through the fog, Kotick climbed a bare rock and looked down on the scattered nurseries and the torn and bleeding seals. 'Now,' he said, 'I've taught you your lesson.'

'My wig!' said old Sea Catch, boosting himself up stiffly, for he was fearfully mauled. 'The Killer Whale himself could not have cut them up worse. Son, I'm proud of you, and what's more, I'll come with you to your island—if there is such a place.'

'Here you, fat pigs of the sea! Who comes with me to the Sea Cow's tunnel? Answer, or I shall teach you again,' roared Kotick.

There was a murmur like the ripple of the tide all up and down the beaches. 'We will come,' said thousands of tired voices, 'We will follow Kotick, the White Seal.'

Then Kotick dropped his head between his shoulders and shut his eyes proudly. He was not a white seal any more, but red from head to tail. All the same, he would have scorned to look at or touch one of his wounds.

A week later he and his army (nearly ten thousand holluschickie and old seals) went away north to the Sea Cow's tunnel, Kotick leading them, and the seals that stayed at Novastoshnah called them idiots. But next spring, when they all met off the fishing-banks of the Pacific, Kotick's seals told such tales of the new beaches beyond Sea Cow's tunnel that more and more seals left Novastoshnah.

Of course it was not all done at once, for the seals need a long time to turn things over in their minds, but year by year more seals went away from Novastoshnah, and Lukannon, and the other nurseries, to the quiet, sheltered beaches where Kotick sits all the summer through, getting bigger and fatter and stronger each year, while the holluschickie play round him, in that sea where no man comes.

WILLIAM AND THE PRIZE CAT

Richmal Crompton

William and Ginger ambled slowly down the lane. Henry and Douglas had succumbed to a local epidemic of mumps and so William and Ginger were the only two representatives of the Outlaws at large. Each carried sticks and slashed at the grass by the roadside as he went along. The action was purely mechanical. Neither felt properly dressed out of doors unless he had a stick to slash at things with.

'Couldn't we get underneath the flap?' Ginger was saying.

'No,' said William, 'I thought of that. They've got someone there to stop you. Jimmy Barlow says he tried that yesterday, and it wasn't any good.'

'You asked your father for money, din't you?' said Ginger.

'Yes,' replied William bitterly, 'and he said that he'd give me some if ever he noticed me being clean and tidy and quiet for three days together. That's a jolly mean way of sayin' "no". 'Sides, if ever I was like that there prob'ly wouldn't be any circus here so it would all be wasted and if there was I bet I wouldn't feel like goin' to it if I'd been clean and tidy and quiet for three days. I bet you wouldn't feel much like doin' anythin' if you'd been clean and tidy and quiet for three days. You asked your father, too, din't you?'

'Yes,' said Ginger gloomily, 'an' he went on and on and on about every window or anythin' that had got broke in our house for—for all my life I should think. He even remembered that time that I fell through the roof and broke the skylight. Well, that's so long ago I'd almost quite forgot that till he said about it. Anyway I hurt myself jolly badly over it an' you'd have thought he'd've been sorry instead of makin' it an excuse not to give me money to go an' see a circus.'

'We haven't even anythin' we can sell,' said William taking up the antiphonic lament. 'I tried to sell my whistle to Frankie Dakers, but it hasn't any whistle in and he wouldn't buy it. He'd been to the circus.'

'Jolly fine one, isn't it?' said Ginger wistfully.

'He said it was a rippin' one,' said William. They walked on for a moment in silence, frowning and slashing absently at the roadside with their sticks.

Then suddenly round a bend in the roadway, all unprepared and unexpecting, they ran into the Hubert Laneites, their rivals and enemies from time immemorial. Hubert Lane, standing in the centre of his little band, smiled fatly at them. It happened to be a period of armed neutrality between the two bands. Had it been a period of open warfare the Hubert Laneites would have fled on sight of even two of the Outlaws, for the Hubert Laneites, though possessed of deep cunning, lacked courage and strength in open warfare. But as it was, Hubert Lane smiled at them fatly.

'Hello,' he said, 'been to the circus?'

Hubert Lane had a knack of finding out most things about his enemies, and he was well aware that the Outlaws had not been to the circus, because they had not enough money for their entrance fee.

'Circus?' said William carelessly. 'What circus?'

'Why the one over at Little Marleigh?' said Hubert, slightly deflated.

'Oh *that* one,' said William smiling, 'you mean *that* one. It's not much of a circus, is it?'

Hubert Lane had recourse to heavy sarcasm.

'Oh no,' he said. 'It takes a much grander circus than *that* to satisfy *you*, I s'pose?'

'Well,' said William mysteriously, 'I know a jolly sight more about circuses than *most* people.'

The Hubert Laneites laughed mockingly.

'*How* do you know more about circuses than most people?' challenged Hubert.

William considered this in silence for a moment, wondering whether to have been in a circus and worked in it till he was rescued and adopted by his present parents, or to have an uncle who owned all the circuses in England and took him to see one every week. He rejected both claims as being too easy for Hubert to disprove, and contented himself with saying still more mysteriously:

'*Wouldn't* you like to know?'

Hubert eyed him uncertainly. He suspected that William's assurance of manner and deep mysteriousness of tone was bluff, and yet he was half impressed by it.

'All right,' retorted William. 'You jolly well wait and see.'

Hubert snorted contemptuously, deciding that this unfounded claim of William's would make a good weapon of offence against him for some time to come, and already framing in his mind simple unvarnished allusions to it as, 'Who said he knew all about circuses an' couldn't afford to go to the one at Little Marleigh?' Such challenges, however, needed to be issued from a safe distance, so for the present he turned to another subject.

'I'm gettin' up a cat show tomorrow,' he said innocently. 'There's a big box of chocolates for the prize. Would you like to bring your cat along?'

The brazen shamelessness of this for a minute took away William's breath. It was well known that Hubert's mother possessed a cat of gigantic proportions, who had won many prizes at shows. That the Hubert Laneites should thus try to win public prestige for themselves, and secure their own box of chocolates by organizing a cat show at which their own exhibit was bound to win the prize was a piece of assurance worthy of them.

'Like to enter your cat?' repeated Hubert carelessly.

William thought of the mangy and undersized creature who represented the sole feline staff of his household. Hubert thought of it too.

'I suppose it wouldn't have much chance,' said Hubert at last, with nauseating pity in his voice.

'It would. It's a jolly fine cat,' said William indignantly.

'Want to enter it then?' said Hubert, satisfied with the cunning that had made William thus court public humiliation. The Brown cat was the worst-looking cat of the village.

'All right,' he said, 'I'll put you down. Bring it along this afternnon.'

William and Ginger walked dejectedly away.

★   ★   ★   ★

Early that afternoon they set off, William carefully carrying the Brown cat, brushed till it was in a state bordering on madness, and adorned with a blue bow (taken off a boudoir cap of Ethel's) at which it tore furiously in the intervals of scratching William.

'It's got spirit, anyway,' said William proudly, 'and that ought to count. It's got more spirit than that fat ole thing of Hubert's mother's. I think spirit ought to count.'

But Ginger refused to be roused from his dejection.

'It doesn't count,' he said. 'I mean it doesn't count *for* them—scratchin' the judges an' such like.' He inspected their entry more closely and his dejection increased. 'Why are there so many places where it hasn't got any fur?'

'It's always like that,' said William. 'It's quite healthy. It eats a lot. But it never has fur on those places. It's all right. It doesn't mean that there's anything wrong with it. It just means that—that it hasn't got fur on those places.'

'And look at its ear. It's gone funny.'

'That's where it had a fight,' explained William, 'it goes out fighting every night. It's a jolly brave cat. I bet there's not many cats that fight as much as this one does.'

As if to corroborate his statement, the cat shot out a paw and gave him a scratch from forehead to chin, then, taking advantage of his suddenly relaxed hold, leapt from his arms and fled down the road still tearing madly at its blue bow.

'There!' said Ginger. 'Now you've gone and done it. Now we've got to go without a cat or not go at all, and they'll laugh at us if we go without a cat, and they'll call us funks if we don't go at all.'

William considered these alternatives gloomily.

'An' they'll go on and on 'cause they know we can't go to the circus,' he added.

'Go after it and try and catch it again,' suggested Ginger.

'No, I'm jolly well not going to,' said William. 'I'm sick of it. I'd rather fight someone.'

'Well, what shall we do?' said Ginger. 'Go without a cat or just not go?'

'Let's sit down and wait a bit,' said William, 'an' try'n think of a plan. We might find a stray cat bigger'n theirs. Let's jus' sit down an' think.'

Ginger shook his head at William's optimism.

'I bet there aren't any stray cats nowadays. I never see any. And if there were they wouldn't just come when you wanted them. And if they did they wouldn't be the big fat sort of cat what like the Lane cat is.'

They were sitting down on the roadside, their backs to the wood that bordered the road. William turned to look into the wood.

'There's wild cats anyway,' he said, 'I bet there's still a few wild cats left in England. I bet *they're* bigger than his mother's old cat. I bet that if we could find a wild cat and tame it and take it along it'd get the prize all right. I shun't be a bit surprised if there was some wild cats left in this wood. I'm goin' to have a look anyway.'

And he was just going to make his way through the hedge that bordered the wood when the most amazing thing happened. Out of the wood gambolling playfully came a gigantic—was it a cat? It was certainly near enough to a cat to be called a cat. But it was far from wild. It greeted Ginger and William affectionately, rolling over on to its back and offering itself to be stroked and rubbed.

They stared at it in amazement.

'It's a wild cat,' said William, 'a tame, wild cat. P'raps hunger made it tame, or perhaps now that there aren't any other wild animals to fight wild cats have got tame. P'raps it's the last wild cat left in England. Puss! Puss! Puss!'

It leapt upon him affectionately.

'It's a *jolly* fine wild cat,' he said, stroking it, 'and we're jolly lucky to have found a cat like this. Look at it. It *knows* it belongs to us now. Let's find something for it to eat.'

'We'd better take it to the show first,' said Ginger, 'it's nearly time.'

So they made a collar for it by tying Ginger's tie loosely round its neck, and a lead by taking a boot-lace out of William's boot and attaching it to the tie and set off towards the Lanes' house.

The wild cat ambled along the road with them in friendly fashion. William walked slowly and ungracefully in the laceless boot, but his heart was overflowing with pride and affection for his new pet.

'I bet it's the finest wild cat anyone's ever found,' he said.

The show was to be held in the shed at the back of the Lane's house. The other competitors were all there, holding more or less unwilling exhibits, and in the place of honour was Hubert Lane holding his mother's enormous tabby. But the Lane tabby was a kitten compared with William's wild cat. The assembled competitors stared at it speechlessly as William, with a nonchalant air, took his seat with it amongst them.

'That—that's not a cat,' gasped Hubert Lane.

William had with difficulty gathered his exhibit upon his knee. He challenged them round its head.

'What is it, then?' he said.

They had no answer. It was certainly more like a cat than anything.

''Course it's a cat,' said William, pursuing his advantage.

'Well, whose is it then?' said Hubert indignantly. 'I bet it's not yours.'

'It *is* mine,' said William.

'Well, why've we never seen it before then?' said Hubert.

'D'you think,' said William, 'that we'd let a valu'ble cat like this run about all over the place? Why, this is one of the most famous cats in all the world. We'd have it stole in no time if we let it run about all over the place like an ordin'ry cat. This isn't an ordin'ry cat, this isn't. Let *me* tell you this is one of the most famous cats in all the world, a speshully famous cat that never comes out except to go to shows, and that's won prizes all over the world. An' we don't tell people about it either for fear of it being stole. Well, I've not got much time and I've got to get it back home, so if our cat's bigger'n yours you'd better give me the prize now, 'cause this cat's not used to be kept hangin' about before being give its prize.'

The Hubert Laneites stared at William and his burden limply. It was no good. They had not the resilience to withstand this shock. They sagged visibly, eyes and mouth open to their fullest extent, gazing at the monster who sat calmly on William's knee rubbing its face against his neck affectionately.

Hubert Lane at last roused himself with an effort from his paralysis of amazement. He knew when he had met defeat. He took the large box of chocolates on which the Hubert Laneites had meant to feast that afternoon and handed it to William, still gaping at the prize winner. The other exhibitors cheered. They were not at all sorry to see the Hubert Laneites worsted. William put the box of chocolates under his arm and set off, leading his exhibit and shuffling awkwardly in his laceless boot. It was not till they reached the gate leading to the road that the Hubert Laneites recovered from their stupefaction. They recovered all at the same time and yelled as with one accord.

'Who can't afford to go to the circus? *Yah.*'

William was still drunk with the pride of possession.

'It's a *jolly* fine wild cat,' he said again.

'Where'll we keep it?' said Ginger practically.

'In the old barn,' said William, 'an' we'll not tell anyone about it. They'll only manage to spoil it somehow if they find out. We'll keep it there an' take it out walks in the woods an' bring it food from home to eat. Then I vote we send it in for some real cat shows. I bet it'll win a lot of money. I bet it'll make us millionaires. An' when I'm a millionaire I'm goin' to buy a circus with every sort of animal in the world in it, an' I bet I'll have a jolly fine time.'

The mention of the circus rather depressed them and Ginger, to cheer them up, suggested eating the chocolates. They descended into the ditch (fortunately dry), and sat there with the prize cat between them. It seemed that the prize cat, too, liked chocolates and the three shared them equally, eating one each in turn till the box was finished.

'Well, it's had its tea now,' said Ginger, 'so let's take it straight to the old barn for the night.'

'You don't know that it's had enough,' said William, 'it might want a bit of something else. I bet we get it up to my bedroom without anyone seeing us and give it a bit of something else to eat there. I bet we can easily get it up without anyone seein'.'

They had reached William's house now.

He picked the animal up in both arms and concealing it inadequately in his coat entered the side door in a conspiratorial fashion followed by Ginger. As soon as he had reached the foot of the stairs, however, there came the sound of the opening of his mother's bedroom door and her footsteps on the landing. William turned and fled into the drawing-room still followed by the faithful Ginger.

'We'll just wait here till she's gone,' he whispered.

Her footsteps descended the stairs and unmistakably began to approach the drawing-room.

'Here! Quick!' gasped William plunging behind a Chesterfield that was placed across a corner of the room. The triangular space thus formed was rather inadequate for the accommodation of William, Ginger and the prize cat, but by squeezing themselves together they just managed to get themselves into it.

The door opened almost as soon as they had reached their hiding place and Mrs Brown entered.

'I don't expect she'll stay here,' whispered William breathlessly, holding his pet in both arms to keep it still.

But Mrs Brown closed the door and sat down. From her bedroom window she had caught sight of a visitor coming up the drive and she had come down to the drawing-room in order to receive and dispose of her as quickly as possible.

Almost as soon as she had entered the maid announced 'Miss Messiter,' and a tall lady wearing horn-rimmed spectacles entered and, after greeting her effusively, took her seat on the Chesterfield behind which were William, Ginger and the prize cat.

William was so much occupied in restraining his prize cat as soundlessly as possible that he did not hear what the visitor and his mother were saying till they had been talking for several minutes. Then as his pet seemed to have settled down to sleep on the top of Ginger he turned his attention to what the visitor was saying.

'I *do* hope you'll come,' she was saying. 'I'm trying to get everyone in the village to promise to come. He's a *marvellous* speaker. In the forefront of the movement.'

'Yes?' said Mrs Brown vaguely. 'The movement?'

'I told you, you know,' said the visitor earnestly, 'the Thought Mastery Movement. It's closely allied to Christian Science, of course, but it's wider. It embraces more spheres, so to speak. It begins with that of pain, of course, teaching that there's no such thing. No such thing at all. I never feel pain. Never. Why? Because my thoughts know that there's no such thing as pain so naturally they don't feel it. Never.'

At this moment the prize cat who had made its way under the Chesterfield and discovered one of Miss Messiter's ankles on the other side put out an exploratory paw and touched it with extended claws. Miss Messiter uttered a scream.

'Whatever's the matter? said Mrs Brown.

The visitor was clutching her ankle.

'A sudden excruciating pain,' she said.

'Neuritis perhaps, or arthritis,' suggested Mrs Brown soothingly. 'They do come on suddenly.'

'Where had I got to?' said the visitor, still rubbing her ankle.

'About your never feeling pain,' said Mrs Brown.

'Oh yes . . . well the *reason* I don't feel pain is simply that I've trained my thoughts to ignore it. My thoughts mechanically reject the notion of pain. It's all so simple.'

At this minute the prize cat put out his paw again in order to experience a second time the delicious sensation of sinking his claws through Miss Messiter's woollen stockings into her skin beneath.

'*Whatever's* the matter?' said Mrs Brown when Miss Messiter's scream had died away.

'Another of those excruciating pains,' said Miss Messiter. 'I can't explain it. I've never known anything of the sort before. Excruciating.'

'Neuritis probably,' said Mrs Brown, showing more interest than she had shown in the Thought Mastery Movement. 'I had a cousin who used to have it. It came on just like that.'

But Miss Messiter was looking behind her.

'There's a boy behind the sofa,' she said excitedly, 'and he must have been running pins into my foot.'

'I didn't,' said William rising, partly to refute this accusation and partly in order to prevent the visitor's discoveries extending to Ginger and the prize cat. 'I *never* stuck pins into her foot.'

'But whatever are you doing there at all, William?' said his mother in a bewildered fashion.

'I jus'—jus' happened to be there,' explained William coming out

The assembled competitors stared speechlessly as William took his seat.

into the room, 'when you came in an' I thought I'd jus'—jus' stay there till you'd gone but I never stuck pins in her foot. I couldn't have even if I'd wanted to 'cause I haven't any pins. And what's more,' he continued bitterly, 'I haven't any money to buy any pins even if I wanted some. If I'd got money to buy pins to stick into her foot I'd be going to the circus.'

'How do you account for the excruciating pain that I felt then?' demanded Miss Messiter of him sternly.

'It must be neuritis,' said William's mother. 'I'm sure he didn't stick pins into your foot. He's very troublesome and untidy and I can't think *why* he was behind the sofa but I'm *sure* he wouldn't stick pins into your foot. He's never done anything like that.'

'Then I must go at once and consult a specialist,' said Miss Messiter firmly. 'It was an *excruciating* pain. It came on quite suddenly, then went quite suddenly.'

'I think that's the best plan,' said Mrs Brown deeply sympathetic. 'I know that neuritis can often be cured if you catch it in the early stages.'

'And I shall give up the organisation of the Thought Mastery Campaign. I think that it has been too much for me. I'm highly strung.'

They drifted out into the hall. William cautiously returned to the corner of the room. Ginger was engaged in a fierce struggle with the prize cat who wanted to return to his investigations under the Chesterfield. He wanted to find the thing into which it was so pleasant to sink one's claws. He was uttering soft little growls as he fought with Ginger.

'Let's get him out quick,' said William, 'while they're talkin' at the front door.'

Ginger, who was suffering agonies from cramp and was pinned helplessly beneath the prize cat, said in a muffled voice:

'A'right. You take him off me an' I'll try to get up.'

William bundled his pet under his arm, and followed by the bowed and limping Ginger, went to the open window, scrambled through with a skill born of long practice and made his unobtrusive way through the shrubbery to the hole in the hedge that was the Outlaws' unofficial entrance to William's garden. Ginger was still limping.

'I've got that pain like what she said she'd got,' he said. 'Cruciating like what she said it was. I bet I've caught it off her. It mus' be something infectious. I shun't be surprised if I die of it.'

'I think hers was the cat scratchin' her,' said William.

'Was it?' said Ginger with interest. 'I couldn't see what it was doin'. It'd got one of its hind feet in my mouth an' I couldn't get it out. It's a wonder I'm not choked.'

But his pins and needles were wearing off and the prize cat, gambolling by their side, was so engaging that it gradually ousted every other thought from their minds.

'We'll take it to the old barn,' said William, 'then you go home an' get some food for it. I'd better not go home jus' now 'cause of that woman sayin' I stuck pins into her foot. My mother'll prob'ly want to go on talkin' about it.'

'All right,' said Ginger, 'what'll I get it?'

'Milk an' a bit of bread an' butter an' a bit of cake,' said William.

'Oh yes,' said Ginger sarcastically. 'Why don't you say a bit of roast turkey as well?'

'A'right,' said William, 'if you can find a bit of roast turkey, bring it along. I bet it'd eat it.'

'I'll bring it what I can find with no one catchin' me,' said Ginger. 'It'll depend whether the larder window's open. I can't do more'n that, can I?'

'Get it as much as you can anyway,' said William.

Ginger departed and William amused himself by playing with his prize cat. It was an excellent play-fellow. It made little feints and darts at William. It rolled over on the ground. It ran away and challenged him to catch it. It growled and pretended to fight him. The time passed on wings till Ginger returned. Ginger's arms were full. Evidently the larder window had been open. He was carrying two buns, half an apple pie, and a piece of cheese. And yet, despite this rich haul, his expression was one of deepest melancholy. He placed the things down absently upon a packing-case, and said:

'I met a boy in the road and he'd just met a man and he said that they were looking for a lion cub that had got away from the circus.'

William's face dropped. They both gazed thoughtfully at the prize cat.

'I—I sort of thought it was a lion cub all the time,' said William.

'So did I,' said Ginger hastily.

After a long and pregnant silence, William said in a faraway voice: 'Well—I suppose we've gotter take it back.' He spoke as one whose world has crashed about him. In his mind had been roseate dreams of a future in which every day the lion cub gambolled round his feet, played hide and seek with him and attacked him with growls of mock ferocity. Life without the lion cub stretched grey and dark before him, hardly worth living.

'I s'pose we've gotter,' said Ginger. 'I s'pose it's stealin' if we don't, now that we know.'

They placed the food before the cub and watched it with melancholy tenderness.

It ate the buns, sat on the apple pie and played football with the piece of cheese.

Then they took up the end of William's boot-lace again and set off sorrowfully with it to Little Marleigh.

⋆   ⋆   ⋆   ⋆

The proprietor of the circus received the truant with relief, and complimented the rescuers on its prompt return. They gazed at it sadly, Ginger replacing his tie and William his boot-lace.

'He's a cute little piece, isn't he?' said the proprietor. 'Don't appear yet. Too young. But goin' to lap up tricks like milk soon . . . Well, I'd better be gettin' a move on. Early show's jus' goin' to begin. Thank you, young sirs.'

'I s'pose,' said William wistfully, 'I s'pose we couldn't *do* anythin' in the show?'

The proprietor scratched his head.

'What c'n you do?' he said.

'I c'n stand on my hands,' said William, 'an' Ginger can pull funny faces. Jolly funny ones.'

The proprietor shook his head.

'Not in our line,' he said. 'But—tell you what. I *am* short-handed, as it happens. A man jus' come over queer an' gone home. We could do with another hand. Jus' movin' things off an' on between turns. Care to help with that?'

So deep was their emotion that William broke his boot-lace and Ginger nearly throttled himself with his tie.

'I should—jolly well—think—we would,' said William hoarsely.

★　　★　　★　　★

The Hubert Laneites sat together in the front row. They'd all been to the circus earlier in the week but they'd come again for this last performance, partly in order to be able to tell the Outlaws that they'd been twice and partly to comfort themselves for the fiasco of their cat show.

'I say,' said Hubert Lane to Bertie Franks, 'I say, won't ole William be mad when we tell him we've been again?'

'Yah,' said Bertie Franks, 'an' I say, fancy him havin' the cheek to say he knew more about circuses than us an' not even been once. We won't half rag him about it. We—'

His voice died away. He stared down into the ring. For there unmistakably was William setting out the little tubs on which the performing ponies performed. He rubbed his eyes and looked again. He hadn't been mistaken. It was William.

'Golly!' he said faintly.

All the Hubert Laneites were staring at William, paralysed with amazement.

'Golly!' they echoed and drew another deep breath as Ginger appeared carrying the chairs on which the clown pretended to do acrobatic feats. Then the circus began. The Hubert Laneites did not see the circus at all. They were staring fascinated at the opening of the tent into which William and Ginger had vanished. After the first turn they emerged and moved away the little tubs and brought out a lot of letters which they laid on the ground for the talking horse to spell from. After that turn William came out alone and held a hoop for Nellie, the Wonder Dog to jump through.

Not once did the expression of stupefied amazement fade from the faces of the Hubert Laneites.

After the circus they walked home dazedly as if in a dream.

★　　★　　★　　★

The next day they approached William cautiously, and with something of reverence in their expressions.

'I say, William,' Hubert said humbly, 'tell us about it, will you?'

'About what?' said William.

'About you helpin' at the circus.'

'Oh *that*,' said William carelessly. 'Oh, I gen'rally help at circuses round about here. I don't always go into the ring like what I did yesterday, but I'm gen'rally in the tent behind helpin' with the animals. Trainin' them for their tricks. Gettin' 'em ready an' such-like. I suppose that one circus tells another about me and that's why they're always askin' me to help. I *said* I knew a jolly sight more about circuses than what you did, you remember.'

'Yes,' said Hubert Lane still more humbly, 'it must be jolly fun, isn't it, William?'

'Oh, it's all right,' said William, 'it's hard work an' of course it's jolly dangerous. Trainin' the animals an' lockin' 'em up for the night an' such-like.' He walked a few yards with an ostentatious limp, and then said, 'the elephant trod on my foot yesterday when I was puttin' it in its cage'—and he touched the scratch that his mother's cat had made. It was certainly quite a showy affair—'the bear gave me this the other night when I was combin' it out ready to go on and do its tricks. It's work not everyone would like to do.'

They gazed at him as at a being from another and a higher sphere.

'I say, William,' said Bertie Franks, 'if—if they want anyone else to help you—you'll give us a chance won't you?'

'I don't s'pose they will,' said William. ''Sides this circus has gone now and I don't know when another's comin'. It's dangerous work, you know, but I'm used to it.'

And, followed by their admiring eyes, he limped elaborately away.

He was limping with the other foot this time, but, of course, no one noticed that.

THE GREY CUB

Jack London

He was different from his brothers and sisters. Their hair already betrayed the reddish hue inherited from their mother, the she-wolf; while he alone, in this particular, took after his father. He was the one little grey cub of the litter. He had bred true to the straight wolf-stock—in fact, he had bred true to old One Eye himself, physically with but a single exception, and that was he had two eyes to his father's one.

The grey cub's eyes had not been opened long, yet already he could see with steady clearness. And while his eyes were still closed, he had felt, tasted, and smelled. He knew his two brothers and his two sisters very well. He had begun to romp with them in a feeble, awkward way, and even to squabble, his little throat vibrating with a queer rasping noise (the forerunner of the growl), as he worked himself into a passion. And long before his eyes had opened, he had learned by touch, taste, and smell to know his mother—a fount of warmth and liquid food and tenderness. She possessed a gentle, caressing tongue that soothed him when it passed over his soft little body, and that impelled him to snuggle close against her and to doze off to sleep.

Most of the first month of his life had been passed thus in sleeping; but now he could see quite well, and he stayed awake for longer periods of time, and he was coming to learn his world quite well. His world was gloomy; but he did not know that, for he knew no other world. It was dim-lighted; but his eyes had never had to adjust themselves to any other light. His world was very small. Its limits were the walls of the lair; but as he had no knowledge of the wide world outside, he was never oppressed by the narrow confines of his existence.

But he had early discovered that one wall of his world was different from the rest. This was the mouth of the cave and the source of light. He had discovered that it was different from the other walls long before he had thoughts of his own, any conscious volitions. It had been an irresistible attraction before ever his eyes opened and looked upon it. The light from it had beat upon his sealed lids, and the eyes and the optic nerves had pulsated to little, sparklike flashes, warm coloured and strangely pleasing. The life of his body, and of every fibre of his body, the life that was the very substance of his body and that was apart from his own personal life, had yearned toward this light and urged his body toward it in the same way that the cunning chemistry of a plant urges it toward the sun.

Always, in the beginning, before his conscious life dawned he had crawled toward the mouth of the cave. And in this his brothers and sisters were one with him. Never, in that period, did any of them crawl toward the dark corners of the back-wall. The light drew them as if they were plants; the chemistry of the life that composed them demanded the light as a necessity of being; and their little puppet-bodies crawled blindly and chemically, like the tendrils of a vine. Later on, when each developed individuality and became personally conscious of impulsions and desires, the attraction of the light increased. They were always crawling and sprawling toward it, and being driven back from it by their mother.

It was in this way that the grey cub learned other attributes of his mother than the soft, soothing tongue. In his insistent crawling toward the light, he discovered in her a nose that with a sharp nudge administered rebuke, and later, a paw, that crushed him down and rolled him over and over with swift, calculating stroke. Thus he learned hurt; and on top of it he learned to avoid hurt, first, by not incurring the risk of it; and second, when he had incurred the risk, by dodging and by retreating. These were conscious actions, and were the results of his first generalisations upon the world. Before that he recoiled automatically from hurt, as he had crawled automatically toward the light. After that he recoiled from hurt because he *knew* that it was hurt.

He was a fierce little cub. So were his brothers and sisters. It was to be expected. He was a carnivorous animal. He came of a breed of meat-killers and meat-eaters. His father and mother lived wholly upon meat. The milk he had sucked with his first flickering life, was milk transformed directly from meat, and now, at a month old, when his eyes had been open for but a week, he was beginning himself to eat meat—meat half-digested by the she-wolf and disgorged for the five growing cubs that already made too great a demand upon her breast.

But he was, further, the fiercest of the litter. He could make a louder rasping growl than any of them. His tiny rages were much more terrible than theirs. It was he that first learned the trick of rolling a fellow-cub over with a cunning paw-stroke. And it was he that first gripped another cub by the ear and pulled and tugged and growled through jaws tight-clenched. And certainly it was he that caused the mother the most trouble in keeping her litter from the mouth of the cave.

The fascination of the light for the grey cub increased from day to day. He was perpetually departing on yard-long adventures toward the cave's entrance, and as perpetually being driven back. Only he did not know it for an entrance. He did not know anything about entrances—passages whereby one goes from one place to another place. He did not know any other place, much less of a way to get there. So to him the entrance of the cave was a wall—a wall of light. As the sun was to the outside dweller, this wall was to him the sun of his world. It attracted him as a candle attracts a moth. He was always striving to attain it. The life that was swiftly expanding within him, urged him continually towards the wall of light. The life that was within him knew that it was the one way out, the way he was predestined to tread. But he himself did not know anything about it. He did not know there was any outside at all.

There was one strange thing about this wall of light. His father (he had already come to recognize his father as the one other dweller in the world, a creature like his mother, who slept near the light and was a bringer of meat)—his father had a way of walking right into the white far wall and disappearing. The grey cub could not understand this. Though never permitted by his mother to approach that wall, he had approached the other walls, and encountered hard obstruction on the end of his tender nose. This hurt. And after several such adventures, he left the walls alone. Without thinking about it, he accepted this disappearing into the wall as a peculiarity of his father, as milk and half-digested meat were peculiarities of his mother.

In fact, the grey cub was not given to thinking—at least, to the kind of thinking customary of men. His brain worked in dim ways. Yet his conclusions were as sharp and distinct as those achieved by men. He had a method of accepting things, without questioning the why and wherefore. In reality, this was the act of classification. He was never disturbed over *why* a thing happened. *How* it happened was sufficient for him. Thus, when he had bumped his nose on the back-wall a few times, he accepted that he would not disappear into walls. In the same way he accepted that his father could disappear into walls. But he was not in the least disturbed by desire to find out the reason for the difference between his father and himself. Logic and physics were no part of his mental make-up.

Like most creatures of the Wild, he early experienced famine. There came a time when not only did the meat supply cease, but the milk no longer came from his mother's breast. At first, the cubs whimpered and cried, but for the most part they slept. It was not long before they were reduced to a coma of hunger. There were no more spats and squabbles, no more tiny rages nor attempts at growling; while the adventures toward the far white wall ceased altogether. The cubs slept, while the life that was in them flickered and died down.

One Eye was desperate. He ranged far and wide, and slept but little in the lair that had now become cheerless and miserable. The she-wolf, too, left her litter and went out in search of meat. In the first days after the birth of the cubs, One Eye had journeyed several times back to the Indian camp, and robbed the rabbit snares; but, with the melting of the snow and the opening of the streams, the Indian camp had moved away, and that source of supply was closed to him.

When the grey cub came back to life and again took interest in the far white wall, he found that the population of his world had been reduced. Only one sister remained to him. The rest were gone. As he grew stronger, he found himself compelled to play alone, for the sister no longer lifted her head nor moved about. His little body rounded out with the meat he now ate; but the food had come too late for her. She slept continuously, a tiny skeleton flung round with skin in which the flame flickered lower and lower and at last went out.

Then there came a time when the grey cub no longer saw his father appearing and disappearing in the wall nor lying down asleep in the entrance. This had happened at the end of a second and less severe famine. The she-wolf knew why One Eye never came back, but there was no way by which she could tell what she had seen to the grey cub. Hunting herself for meat, up the left fork of the stream where lived the lynx, she had followed a day-old trail of One Eye. And she had found him, or what remained of him, at the end of the trail. There were many signs of the battle that had been fought, and of the lynx's withdrawal to her lair after having won the victory. Before she went away, the she-wolf had found this lair, but the signs told her that the lynx was inside, and she had not dared to venture in.

After that, the she-wolf in her hunting avoided the left fork. For she knew that in the lynx's lair was a litter of kittens, and she knew the lynx for a fierce, bad-tempered creature and a terrible fighter. It was all very well for half a dozen wolves to drive a lynx, spitting and bristling, up a tree; but it was quite a different matter for a lone wolf to encounter a lynx—especially when the lynx was known to have a litter of hungry kittens at her back.

But the Wild is the Wild, and motherhood is motherhood, at all times fiercely protective whether in the Wild or out of it; and the time was to come when the she-wolf, for her grey cub's sake, would venture the left fork, and the lair in the rocks, and the lynx's wrath.

★   ★   ★   ★

By the time his mother began leaving the cave on hunting expeditions, the cub had learned well the law that forbade his approaching the entrance. Not only had this law been forcibly and many times impressed on him by his mother's nose and paw, but in him the instinct of fear was developing. Never, in his brief cave-life, had he encountered anything of which to be afraid. Yet fear was in him. It had come down to him from a remote ancestry through a thousand lives. It was a heritage he had received directly from One Eye and the she-wolf; but to them, in turn, it had been passed down through all the generations of wolves that had gone before. Fear!—that legacy of the Wild which no animal may escape nor exchange for pottage.

So the grey cub knew fear, though he knew not the stuff of which fear was made. Possibly he accepted it as one of the restrictions of life. For he had already learned that there were such restrictions. Hunger he had known; and when he could not appease his hunger he had felt restriction. The hard obstruction of the cave-wall, the sharp nudge of his mother's nose, the smashing stroke of her paw, the hunger unappeased of several famines, had borne in upon him that all was not freedom in the world, that to life there were limitations and restraints. These limitations and restraints were laws. To be obedient to them was to escape hurt and make for happiness.

He did not reason the question out in this man fashion. He merely classified the things that hurt and the things that did not hurt. And after such classification he avoided the things that hurt, the restrictions and restraints, in order to enjoy the satisfactions and the remunerations of life.

Thus it was that in obedience to the law laid down by his mother, and in obedience to the law of that unknown and nameless thing, fear, he kept away from the mouth of the cave. It remained to him a white wall of light. When his mother was absent, he slept most of the time, while during the intervals that he was awake he kept very quiet, suppressing the whimpering cries that tickled in his throat and strove for noise.

Once, lying awake, he heard a strange sound in the white wall. He did not know that it was a wolverine, standing outside, all a-trembling with its own daring, and cautiously scenting out the contents of the cave. The cub knew only that the sniff was strange, a something unclassified, therefore unknown and terrible—for the unknown was one of the chief elements that went into the making of fear.

The hair bristled up on the grey cub's back, but it bristled silently. How was he to know that this thing that sniffed was a thing at which to bristle? It was not born of any knowledge of his, yet it was the visible expression of the fear that was in him, and for which, in his own life, there was no accounting. But fear was accompanied by another instinct—that of concealment. The cub was in a frenzy of terror, yet he lay without movement or sound, frozen, petrified into immobility, to all appearances dead. His mother, coming home, growled as she smelt the wolverine's track, and bounded into the cave and licked and nozzled him with undue vehemence of affection. And the cub felt that somehow he had escaped a great hurt.

But there were other forces at work in the cub, the greatest of which was growth. Instinct and law demanded of him obedience. But growth demanded disobedience. His mother and fear impelled him to keep away from the white wall. Growth is life, and life is for ever destined to make for light. So there was no damming up the tide of life that was rising within him—rising with every mouthful of meat he swallowed, with every breath he drew. In the end, one day, fear and obedience were swept away by the rush of life, and the cub straddled and sprawled toward the entrance.

Unlike any other wall with which he had had experience, this wall seemed to recede from him as he approached. No hard surface collided with the tender little nose he thrust out tentatively before him. The substance of the wall seemed as permeable and yielding as light. And as condition, in his eyes, had the seeming of form, so he entered into what had been wall to him and bathed in the substance that composed it.

It was bewildering. He was sprawling through solidity. And ever the light grew brighter. Fear urged him to go back, but growth drove him on. Suddenly he found himself at the mouth of the cave. The wall, inside which he had thought himself, as suddenly leaped back before him to an immeasurable distance. The light had become painfully bright. He was dazzled by it. Likewise he was made dizzy by this abrupt and tremendous extension of space. Automatically, his eyes were adjusting themselves to the brightness, focusing themselves to meet the increased distance of objects. At first, the wall had leaped beyond his vision. He now saw it again; but it had taken upon itself a remarkable remoteness. Also, its appearance had changed. It was now a variegated wall, composed of the trees that fringed the stream, the opposing mountain that towered above the trees, and the sky that out-towered the mountain.

A great fear came upon him. This was more of the terrible unknown. He crouched down on the lip of the cave and gazed out on the world. He was very much afraid. Because it was unknown, it was hostile to him. Therefore the hair stood up on end along his back and his lips wrinkled weakly in an attempt at a ferocious and intimidating snarl. Out of his puniness and fright he challenged and menaced the whole wide world.

Nothing happened. He continued to gaze, and in his interest he forgot to snarl. Also, he forgot to be afraid. For the time, fear had been routed by growth, while growth had assumed the guise of curiosity. He began to notice near objects—an open portion of the stream that flashed in the sun, the blasted pine-tree that stood at the base of the slope, and the slope itself, that ran right up to him and ceased two feet beneath the lip of the cave on which he crouched.

Now the grey cub had lived all his days on a level floor. He had never experienced the hurt of a fall. He did not know what a fall was. So he stepped boldly out upon the air. His hind-legs still rested on the cave-lip, so he fell forward head downward. The earth struck him a harsh blow on the nose that made him yelp. Then he began rolling down the slope, over and over. He was in a panic of terror. The unknown had caught him at last. It had gripped savagely hold of him and was about to wreak upon him a terrific hurt. Growth was now routed by fear, and he ki-ki'd like any frightened puppy.

The unknown bore him on he knew not to what frightful hurt, and he yelped and ki-ki'd unceasingly. This was a different proposition from crouching in frozen fear while the unknown lurked just alongside. Now the unknown had caught tight hold of him. Silence would do no good. Besides, it was not fear, but terror, that convulsed him.

But the slope grew more gradual, and its base was grass-covered. Here the cub lost momentum. When at last he came to a stop, he gave one last agonized yelp and then a long, whimpering wail. Also, and quite as a matter of course, as though in his life he had already made a thousand toilets, he proceeded to lick away the dry clay that soiled him.

After that he sat up and gazed about him, as might the first man of the earth who landed upon Mars. The cub had broken through the wall of the world, the unknown had let go its hold of him, and here he was without hurt. But the first man on Mars would have experienced less unfamiliarity than did he. Without any antecedent knowledge, without any warning whatever that such existed, he found himself an explorer in a totally new world.

Now that the terrible unknown had let go of him he forgot that the unknown had any terrors. He was aware only of curiosity in all the things about him. He inspected the grass beneath him, the moss-berry plant just beyond, and the dead trunk of the blasted pine that stood on the edge of an open space among the trees. A squirrel, running around the base of the trunk, came full upon him, and gave him a fright. He cowered down and snarled. But the squirrel was as badly scared. It ran up the tree, and from a point of safety chattered back savagely.

This helped the cub's courage, and though the woodpecker he next encountered gave him a start, he proceeded confidently on his way. Such was his confidence, that when a moose-bird impudently hopped up to him, he reached out at it with a playful paw. The result was a sharp peck on the end of his nose that made him cower down and ki-ki. The noise he made was too much for the moose-bird, who sought safety in flight.

But the cub was learning. His misty little mind had already made an unconscious classification. There were live things and things not alive. Also, he must watch out for the live things. The things not alive remained always in one place; but the live things moved about, and there was no telling what they might do. The thing to expect of them was the unexpected, and for this he must be prepared.

He travelled very clumsily. He ran into sticks and things. A twig that he thought a long way off, would the next instant hit him on the nose or rake along his ribs. There were inequalities of surface. Sometimes he overstepped and stubbed his nose. Quite as often he understepped and stubbed his feet. Then there were the pebbles and stones that turned under him when he trod upon them; and from them he came to know that the things not alive were not all in the same state of stable equilibrium as was his cave; also, that small things not alive were more liable than large things to fall down or turn over. But with every mishap he was learning. The longer he walked the better he walked. He was adjusting himself. He was learning to calculate his own muscular movements, to know his physical limitations, to measure distances between objects, and between objects and himself.

His was the luck of the beginner. Born to be a hunter of meat (though he did not know it), he blundered upon meat just outside his own cave-door on his first foray into the world. It was by sheer blundering that he chanced upon the shrewdly hidden ptarmigan nest. He fell into it. He had essayed to walk upon the trunk of a fallen pine. The rotten bark gave way under his feet, and with a despairing yelp he pitched down the rounded descent, smashed through the leafage and stalks of a small bush, and in the heart of the bush, on the ground, fetched up in the midst of the seven ptarmigan chicks.

They made noises, and at first he was frightened at them. Then he perceived that they were very little, and he became bolder. They moved. He placed his paw on one, and its movements were accelerated. This was a source of enjoyment to him. He smelled it. He picked it up in his mouth. It struggled and tickled his tongue. At the same time he was made aware of a sensation of hunger. His jaws closed together. There was a crunching of fragile bones, and warm blood ran in his mouth. The taste of it was good. This was meat, the same as his mother gave him, only it was alive between his teeth and therefore better. So he ate the ptarmigan. Nor did he stop till he had devoured the whole brood. Then he licked his chops in quite the same way his mother did, and began to crawl out of the bush.

He encountered a feathered whirlwind. He was confused and blinded by the rush of it and the beat of angry wings. He hid his head between his paws and yelped. The blows increased. The mother-ptarmigan was in a fury. Then he became angry. He rose up, snarling, striking out with his paws. He sank his tiny teeth into one of the wings and pulled and tugged sturdily. The ptarmigan struggled against him, showering blows upon him with her free wing. It was his first battle. He was elated. He forgot all about the unknown. He no longer was afraid of anything. He was fighting, tearing at a live thing that was striking at him. Also, this live thing was meat. The lust to kill was on him. He had just destroyed little live things. He would now destroy a big live thing. He was too busy and happy to know that he was happy. He was thrilling and exulting in ways new to him and greater to him than any he had known before.

98

With a despairing yelp he rolled down into a nest of chicks.

He held on to the wing and growled between his tight-clenched teeth. The ptarmigan dragged him out of the bush. When she turned and tried to drag him back into the bush's shelter, he pulled her away from it and on into the open. And all the time she was making outcry and striking with her free wing, while feathers were flying like a snowfall. The pitch to which he was aroused was tremendous. All the fighting blood of his breed was up in him and surging through him. This was living, though he did not know it. He was realising his own meaning in the world; he was doing that for which he was made —killing meat and battling to kill it. He was justifying his existence, than which life can do no greater; for life achieves its summit when it does to the uttermost that which it was equipped to do.

After a time the ptarmigan ceased her struggling. He still held her by the wing, and they lay on the ground and looked at each other. He tried to growl threateningly, ferociously. She pecked on his nose, which by now, what of previous adventures, was sore. He winced but held on. She pecked him again and again. From wincing he went to whimpering. He tried to back away from her, oblivious to the fact that by his hold on her he dragged her after him. A rain of pecks fell on his ill-used nose. The flood of fight ebbed down in him, and releasing his prey, he turned tail and scampered off across the open in inglorious retreat.

He lay down to rest on the other side of the open, near the edge of the bushes, his tongue lolling out, his chest heaving and panting, his nose still hurting him and causing him to continue to whimper. But as he lay there, suddenly there came to him a feeling as of something terrible impending. The unknown with all its terrors rushed upon him, and he shrank back instinctively into the shelter of the bush. As he did so, a draught of air fanned him, and a large, winged body swept ominously and silently past. A hawk, driving down out of the blue, had barely missed him.

While he lay in the bush recovering from this fright and peering fearfully out, the mother-ptarmigan on the other side of the open space fluttered out of the ravaged nest. It was because of her loss that she paid no attention to the winged bolt of the sky. But the cub saw, and it was a warning and a lesson to him—the swift downward swoop of the hawk, the short skim of its body just above the ground, the strike of its talons in the body of the ptarmigan, the ptarmigan's squawk of agony and fright, and the hawk's rush upward into the blue, carrying the ptarmigan away with it.

It was a long time before the cub left his shelter. He had learned much. Live things were meat. They were good to eat. Also, live things when they were large enough, could give hurt. It was better to eat small live things like ptarmigan chicks, and to let alone large live things like ptarmigan hens. Nevertheless he felt a little prick of ambition, a sneaking desire to have another battle with that ptarmigan hen—only the hawk had carried her away. Maybe there were other ptarmigan hens. He would go and see.

He came down a shelving bank to the stream. He had never seen water before. The footing looked good. There were no inequalities of surface. He stepped boldly out on it; and went down, crying with fear, into the embraces of the unknown. It was cold, and he gasped, breathing quickly. The water rushed into his lungs instead of the air that had always accompanied his act of breathing. The suffocation he experienced was like the pang of death. To him it signified death. He had no conscious knowledge of death, but like every animal of the Wild, he possessed the instinct of death. To him it stood as the greatest of hurts. It was the very essence of the unknown; it was the sum of the terrors of the unknown, the one culminating and unthinkable catastrophe that could happen to him, about which he knew nothing and about which he feared everything.

He came to the surface, and the sweet air rushed into his open mouth. He did not go down again. Quite as though it had been a long-established custom of his he struck out with all his legs and began to swim. The near bank was a yard away; but he had come up with his back to it, and the first thing his eyes rested upon was the opposite bank, toward which he immediately began to swim. The stream was a small one, but in the pool it widened out to a score of feet.

Midway in the passage, the current picked up the cub and swept him down stream. He was caught in the miniature rapid at the bottom of the pool. Here was little chance for swimming. The quiet water had become suddenly angry. Sometimes he was under, sometimes on top. At all times he was in violent motion, now being turned over or around, and again, being smashed against a rock. And with every rock he struck, he yelped. His progress was a series of yelps, from which might have been adduced the number of rocks he encouraged.

Below the rapid was a second pool, and here, captured by the eddy, he was gently borne to the bank and as gently deposited on a bed of gravel. He crawled frantically clear of the water and lay down. He had learned some more about the world. Water was not any solidity at all. His conclusion was that things were not always what they appeared to be. The cub's fear of the unknown was an inherited distrust, and it had now been strengthened by experience. Thenceforth, in the nature of things, he would possess an abiding distrust of appearances. He would have to learn the reality of a thing before he could put his faith into it.

One other adventure was destined for him that day. He had recollected that there was such a thing in the world as his mother. And then there came to him a feeling that he wanted her more than all the rest of the things in the world. Not only was his body tired with the adventures it had undergone, but his little brain was equally tired. In all the days he had lived it had not worked so hard as on this one day. Furthermore, he was sleepy. So he started out to look for the cave and his mother, feeling at the same time an overwhelming rush of loneliness and helplessness.

He was sprawling along between some bushes, when he heard a sharp intimidating cry. There was a flash of yellow before his eyes. He saw a weasel leaping swiftly away from him. It was a small live thing, and he had no fear. Then, before him, at his feet, he saw an extremely small live thing, only several inches long, a young weasel, that, like himself, had disobediently gone out adventuring. It tried to retreat before him. He turned it over with his paw. It made a queer, grating noise. The next moment the flash of yellow reappeared before his eyes. He heard again the intimidating cry, and at the same instant received a severe blow on the side of the neck and felt the sharp teeth of the mother-weasel cut into his flesh.

Whilst he yelped and ki-yi'd and scrambled backward, he saw the mother-weasel leap upon her young one and disappear with it into the neighbouring thicket. The cut of her teeth in his neck still hurt, but his feelings were hurt more grievously, and he sat down and weakly whimpered. This mother-weasel was so small and so savage! He was yet to learn that for size and weight the weasel was the most ferocious, vindictive, and terrible of all the killers of the Wild. But a portion of this knowledge was quickly to be his.

He was still whimpering when the mother-weasel reappeared. She did not rush him, now that her young one was safe. She approached more cautiously, and the cub had full opportunity to observe her lean, snakelike body, and her head, erect, eager, and snakelike itself. Her sharp, menacing cry sent the hair bristling along his back, and he snarled warningly at her. She came closer and closer. There was a leap, swifter than his unpractised sight, and the lean, yellow body disappeared for a moment out of the field of vision. The next moment she was at his throat, her teeth buried in his hair and flesh.

At first he snarled and tried to fight; but he was very young, and this was only his first day in the world, and his snarl became a whimper, his fight a struggle to escape. The weasel never relaxed her hold. She hung on, striving to press down with her teeth to the great vein where his life-blood bubbled. The weasel was a drinker of blood, and it was ever her preference to drink from the throat of life itself.

The grey cub would have died, and there would have been no story to write about him, had not the she-wolf come bounding through the bushes. The weasel let go the cub and flashed at the she-wolf's throat, missing, but getting a hold on the jaw instead. The she-wolf flirted her head like the snap of a whip, breaking the weasel's hold and flinging it high in the air. And, still in the air, the she-wolf's jaws closed on the lean, yellow body, and the weasel knew death between the crunching teeth.

The cub experienced another excess of affection on the part of his mother. Her joy at finding him seemed greater even than his joy at being found. She nozzled him and caressed him and licked the cuts made in him by the weasel's teeth. Then, between them, mother and cub, they ate the blood-drinker, and after that went back to the cave and slept.

MAXWELL'S OTTER

Gavin Maxwell

After the death of his dog, Johnnie, Gavin Maxwell decided that he would never own a dog again. However, the lonely autumn and winter days at Camusféarna, his West Highland sea-board home, made him crave for some animal life about the house. On a journey to Southern Iraq in 1956 he was given an unusual breed of otter, which he called Mijbil—Mij for short. He brought Mij back to London with him. . . .

I lived at that time in a studio flat near to Olympia, one large room with a sleeping gallery that opened on to the garage roof, and penthouse premises at the back containing kitchen, bathroom and box-room, each of diminutive size and resembling a divided corridor. Despite the absence of a garden, these unconventional premises held certain advantages for an otter, for the garage roof eliminated the normal difficulties of keeping a house-trained animal in a London flat, and the box-room opening from the bathroom provided quarters in which at any time he might be left for short periods with all his essential requirements. But just how short those periods would be—a maximum of four or five hours—had never struck me until Mij had already become the centre point round which, eccentrically, revolved my life. Otters that have been reared by human beings demand human company, much affection, and constant co-operative play; without these things they quickly become unhappy, and for the most part they are tiresome in direct ratio to their discontent. They can be trying, too, out of sheer inquisitiveness and exuberance of spirits, but not in the seemingly calculated way that is born of deprivation.

The spacious tile-floored bedroom of the Consulate-General at Basra, with its minimum of inessential furniture or bric-à-brac, had done little to prepare me for the problems that my crowded and vulnerable studio would present in relation to Mijbil. Exhausted as he was that first night, he had not been out of his box for five minutes before he set out with terrifying enthusiasm to explore his new quarters. I had gone to the kitchen to find fish for him, expected by prearrangement with my charlady, but I had hardly got there before I heard the first crash of breaking china in the room behind me. The fish and the bath solved the problem temporarily, for when he had eaten he went wild with joy in the water and romped ecstatically for a full half hour, but it was clear that the flat would require considerable alteration if it was to remain a home for both of us. Meanwhile sleep seemed long overdue, and I saw only one solution; I laid a sleeping bag on the sofa, and anchored Mij to the sofa-leg by his lead.

I have never been able fully to make up my mind whether certain aspects of otter behaviour merely chance to resemble that of human beings, or whether, in the case of animals as young as Mij was, there is actual mimicry of the human foster parent. Mij, anyway, seemed to regard me closely as I composed myself on my back with a cushion under my head; then, with a confiding air of knowing exactly what to do, he clambered up beside me and worked his body down into the sleeping-bag until he lay flat on his back inside it with his head on the cushion beside mine and his fore-paws in the air. In this position, such an attitude as a child devises for its teddy-bear in bed, Mij heaved an enormous sigh and was instantly asleep.

There is, in fact, much about otters that encourages humans to a facile anthropomorphizing. A dry otter at play is an animal that might have been specifically designed to please a child; they look like 'invented' animals, and are really much more like Giovannetti's 'Max' than anything else, a comparison that has instantly struck many people upon seeing my otters for the the first time—the same short legs, the same tubby, furry torso, vast whiskers, and clownish good humour. In the water they take on quite a different aspect and personality, supple as an eel, fast as lightning, and graceful as a ballet dancer, but very few people have watched them for long below the surface, and I have yet to see a zoo that gives its otters a glass-sided tank—a spectacle that I believe would steal the show from the whole aquarium.

★   ★   ★   ★

Mij and I remained in London for nearly a month, while, as my landlord put it, the studio came to look like a cross between a monkey-house and a furniture repository. The garage roof was fenced in, and a wire gate fitted to the gallery stairs, so that he could occasionally be excluded from the studio itself; the upstairs telephone was enclosed in a box (whose fastening he early learned to undo); my dressing-table was cut off from him by a wire flap hinging from the ceiling, and the electric light wires were enclosed in tunnels of hardboard that gave the place the appearance of a power-house.

All these precautions were entirely necessary, for if Mij thought that he had been excluded for too long, more especially from visitors whose acquaintance he wished to make, he would set about laying waste with extraordinary invention. No amount of forethought that I could muster was ever able to forestall his genius; there was always something that I had overlooked, something that could be made to speak with a crash for his mood of frustration, and it did not take me long to learn that prophylaxis was more convenient than treatment.

There was nothing haphazard about the demonstrations he planned; into them went all the patience and ingenuity of his remarkable brain and all the agility of his muscular little body. One evening, for example, after the contractors had departed for the third of fourth time, leaving, as I thought, an otter-proof situation at last, I had confined Mij to the gallery for an hour in deference to the wishes of a female visitor who feared for her nylons. He appeared, after a few moments, balancing adroitly on the top of the gallery railing, paying no attention either to us or to the formidable drop below him, for his plan was evidently already mature. At various points along the length of this railing were suspended certain decorative objects, a

Cretan shepherd's bag, a dagger, and other things whose identity now eludes me. Purposefully, and with an air of enormous self-satisfaction, Mij began to chew through the cords from which these *objets d'art* or *de voyage* hung. After each severance he would pause to watch his victim crash to the parquet floor below, then he would carefully renew his precarious, straddling progress along the rail until he reached the next. We stood, my visitor and I, waiting to catch the more fragile items as they fell, and I remember that when the last fruit, as it were, had fallen from the bough she turned to me with a sigh and said, 'Don't you ever feel that this just simply can't go on?'

More usually, however, when he was loose in the studio, he would play for hours at a time with what soon became an established selection of toys, ping-pong balls, marbles, india-rubber fruit, and a terrapin shell that I brought back from his native marshes. The smaller among these objects he became adept at throwing right across the room with a flick of his head, and with a ping-pong ball he invented a game of his own which would keep him engrossed for up to half an hour at a time. An expanding suitcase that I had taken to Iraq had become damaged on the journey home, so that the lid, when closed, remained at a slope from one end to the other. Mij discovered that if he placed the ball on the high end it would run down the length of the suitcase unaided. He would dash round to the other end to ambush its arrival, hide from it, crouching, to spring up and take it by surprise as it reached the drop to the floor, grab it and trot off with it to the high end once more.

These games were adequate for perhaps half of all the time he spent indoors and awake, but several times a day he needed, as much psychologically as physically, I think, a prolonged romp with a human playmate. Tunnelling under the carpet and affecting to believe himself thus rendered invisible, he would shoot out with a squeak of triumph if a foot passed within range; or he would dive inside the loose cover of the sofa and play tigers from behind it; or he would simply lay seige to one's person as a puppy does, bouncing around one in a frenzy of excited chirps and squeaks and launching a series of tip-and-run raids. It was the 'tip' that was the trouble, for his teeth were like needles, and however gently he might try to use them, such games used, I am bound to say, to end with a certain amount of visible proof of his success in tactics left on the human hand. It did not hurt, but it made a bad impression upon visitors, many of whom were ready in any case to accord him the distrust appropriate to an alien upstart.

But I soon found an infallible way to distract his attention if he became too excitable, a way whose success was, I think, due to the refusal to be baffled by obstacles that is an otter characteristic. I would take the terrapin shell, wrap it in a towel, and knot the loose ends tightly across. He came to know these preparations, and would wait absolutely motionless until I handed him the bundle; then he would straddle it with his forearms, sink his teeth in the knots, and begin to hump and shuffle round the room in a deceptively aimless-seeming manner. Deceptive, because no matter how complex the knots he would have them all undone in five or ten minutes. At the end of this performance he liked, and seemed to expect, applause, and he would then bring the towel and the terrapin shell to be tied up again. He brought the towel first, dragging it, and then made a second trip for the terrapin, shuffling it in front of him down the room like a football.

At night he slept in my bed, still, at this time, on his back with his head on the pillow, and in the morning he shared my bath. With utter indifference to temperature he would plunge ahead of me into water still too hot for me to enter, and while I shaved he would swim round me playing with the soapsuds or with various celluloid and rubber ducks and ships that had begun to accumulate in my bathroom as they do in a child's.

Outside the house I exercised him on a lead, precisely as if he had been a dog, and, like a dog, he soon showed preference for certain streets and certain corners at which dogs of all sorts and sizes had left stimulating messages; messages that were, perhaps the more fascinating for being, as it were, in a foreign language. Whether or not he could decipher their purport, whether or not they conjured up for him the various erotic, impudent or pugnacious images intended, he would spend minutes at a time sniffing these clearing-houses of local canine information, and would occasionally add to them some liquid comment of his own, tantalisingly cryptic, no doubt, to the next comer.

I was too timid of the result to allow him to meet any dog so to speak nose to nose, and I would pick him up if we met unattended dogs in the street, but for his part he seemed largely indifferent to them. The only time that I was conscious of some mutual recognition taking place, some awareness of similarity between canine and lutrine values, was one morning when, setting out for his walk, he refused to be parted from a new toy, a large rubber ball painted in gaudy segments. This ball was too big for his mouth, so that he could only carry it sticking out from one side of his jaws like a gigantic gum boil, and thus encumbered he set off briskly up the street, tugging at his lead. Rounding the first corner we came face to face with a very fat spaniel, unattended and sedately carrying in its mouth a bundle of newspapers. The respective loads of otter and dog made it difficult for either of them to turn its head far as they came abreast, but their eyes rolled sideways with what appeared to me a wild surmise, and when they were a few paces past each other both suddenly stopped dead for a moment, as though arrested by some momentary mental revelation.

Mij quickly developed certain compulsive habits on these walks in the London streets, akin, clearly, to the rituals of children who on their way to and from school must place their feet squarely on the centre of each paving block; must touch every seventh upright of the iron railings, or pass to the outside of every second lamp post. Opposite to my flat was a single-storied primary school, along whose frontage ran a low wall some two feet high separating a corridor-width strip of garden from the road. On his way home, but never on his way out, Mij would tug me in the direction of this wall, jump up on it, and gallop the full length of its thirty yards, to the hopeless distraction both of pupils and of staff within. There was more than one street of which he would use one pavement only, refusing with dug-in toes to be led to the other side, and there were certain drain grilles through which he would peer motionless for long seconds before he could be led away from them. On return to the flat he would scrabble frantically to be let in, and the moment his lead was unhitched he would roll on his back and squirm with eye-bewildering speed and vigour before returning to his toys.

Many of his actions, indeed, appeared ritual, and I think that

Mij shared my bath, playing with the rubber toys while I shaved.

comparatively few people who keep wild creatures realize the enormous security-value of routine in the maintenance of an animal's contentment. As soon as routine is broken a new element enters, in however minute and unrecognizable a trace—the fear of the unknown which is basic to the behaviour of all animals, including man. Every living creature exists by a routine of some kind; the small rituals of that routine are the landmarks, the boundaries of security, the reassuring walls that exclude a *horror vacui*; thus, in our own species, after some tempest of the spirit in which the landmarks seem to have been swept away, a man will reach out tentatively in mental darkness to feel the walls, to assure himself that they still stand where they tood—a necessary gesture, for the walls are of his own building, without universal reality, and what man makes he may destroy. To an animal these landmarks are of even greater importance, for once removed from its natural surroundings, its ecological norm, comparatively little of what the senses perceive can be comprehended in function or potentiality, and the true conditions for insecurity are already established. As among human beings, animal insecurity may manifest itself as aggression or timidity, ill-temper or ill-health, or as excessive affection for a parental figure; unfortunately this last aspect encourages many to cultivate insecurity in their charges, child or animal, as a means to an end.

★　　　★　　　★　　　★

It was about this time that Mij delivered his first serious, intentional bite. He was fed now upon live eels—which I had learned to be the staple food of many races of otter—supplemented by a mixture of raw egg and unpolished rice, a sticky concoction for which he evinced a gusto no doubt influenced by his early life among the Arabs. The eels I kept in a perforated bucket under the kitchen tap, and fed them to him in the bath; it had become an established way of quieting him when he was obstreperous, to shut him in with a full bath of water and three or four eels. On this occasion I had closed the bathroom door imperfectly, and Mij elected to bring his second eel through and eat it in the studio. To this, though he was sodden with water and the eel very slimy, there seemed no alternative, for it is folly to try to take away from a wild animal its natural prey; but when after a few mouthfuls he decided to carry it upstairs to the gallery I determined to call a halt, visualizing a soaking and eel-slimed bed. I put on three pairs of gloves, the outermost being a pair of heavily-padded flying gauntlets. I caught up with him half-way up the stairway; he laid down the eel, put a paw on it, and hummed at me, a high continuous hum that could break out into a wail. Full of euphoric selfconfidence I talked away quietly to him, telling him that he couldn't possibly hurt me and that I was going to take the eel back to the bathroom. The humming became much louder. I bent down and put my heavily-gloved hand upon the eel. He screamed at me, but still he took no action. Then, as I began to lift it, he bit. He bit just once and let go; the canines of his upper and lower jaws passed through the three layers of glove, through the skin, through muscle and bone, and met in the middle of my hand with an audible crunch. He let go almost in the same instant, and rolled on his back squirming with apology. I still held the eel; I carried it back to the bath, where he refused to pay any further attention to it, fussing round me and over me and muzzling me with little squeals of affection and apparent solicitude.

There were two small bones broken in my hand, and for a week it was the size of a boxing glove, very painful, and an acute embarrassment to me in the presence of those who from the first had been sceptical of Mij's domesticity. I had been given a sharp and necessary reminder that though he might carry painted rubber balls through the London streets he was not a spaniel.

It was not lack of curiosity, so much as lack of time and opportunity, that made me delay for nearly three weeks before making any real effort to establish Mij's identity. It would, I thought, require a day's research in the library of the Zoological Society, and at that early stage Mij could not be left alone for more than an hour or so without fretting. But as may be imagined, he caused no small stir in his walks through the streets of West Kensington, and it was increasingly borne in upon me that I could answer only in the most perfunctory and unsatisfactory terms the fire of questions with which our strolls were punctuated.

It is not, I suppose, in any way strange that the average Londoner should not recognize an otter, but the variety of guesses as to what kind of animal this might be came as no less of a surprise to me than the consistent accuracy with which a minority bracketed the bull's-eye without once touching it. Otters belong to a comparatively small group of animals called Mustellines, shared by the badger, mongoose, weasel, stoat, polecat, marten, mink and others; the official at Cairo airport had set an early precedent of outer scoring when he asked whether Mij was an ermine—which is, of course, a stoat in winter coat. Now, in the London streets, I faced a continual barrage of conjectural questions that sprayed all the Mustellines but the otter; wilder, more random fire hit on practically everything from 'a baby seal' to a squirrel. The seal heresy had deep root, and was perhaps the commonest of them all, though far from being the most bizarre; 'Is that a walrus, mister?' reduced me to giggles outside Harrods, and 'a hippo' made my day outside Cruft's Dog Show. A beaver, a bear cub, a newt, a leopard—one, apparently, that had changed his spots—even, with heaven knows what dim recollections of schoolroom science and a bewildering latinized world of sub-human creatures—a 'brontosaur'; Mij was anything but an otter.

But the question for which I awarded the highest score—a question evading with contemptuous dexterity any possible inaccuracy on the part of the speaker; putting the blame, as it were, for the creature's unfamiliarity squarely on my own shoulders; hinting, or doing more than hint, that someone had blundered, that the hand of the potter had shaken; containing, too, an accusation of unfinished work unfit for exhibition—came from a Herculean labourer engaged, mightily and alone, upon digging a hole in the street. I was still far from him when he laid down his pick, put his hands on his hips, and began to stare. As I drew nearer I saw that this state held an outraged quality, one of surprise, certainly, but also of affront, as though he would have me know that he was not one upon whom to play jokes. I came abreast of him; he spat, glared, and then growled out, ''Ere, mister —*what is that supposed to be?*'

It was, I think, his question more than any other that reminded me of my own ignorance; I did not, in fact, know what Mij was supposed to be. I knew, certainly, that he was an otter, but I also knew that he must be one of a species which, if known to the scientific world, was at least not known to live in the delta marshes of the Tigris and Euphrates, for the scant zoological literature that had accompanied me to Iraq made it plain that the only known otter of the Mesopotamian marshes was the Persian sub-species of the common European otter, *Lutra lutra*. Chahala, the cub that had died, had clearly belonged to that race; she had longer fur with 'guard hairs' in place of Mij's sleek, darker velvet; she was lighter on her throat and belly than upon her back, whereas Mij's body seemed to have been slipped into an evenly dyed plush bag; the under side of her tail was not, as was Mij's, flat like a ruler.

In a village of the marshes between the Tigris and the Persian frontier I had bought two otter skins from the householder with whom we had been staying; both were, apart from any possible scientific interest, objects of fascination, for they had been 'case' skinned, the whole carcase having been removed, without a single incision, through the mouth. One of these skins belonged to Chahala's race; the other, contrast heightened by juxtaposition, was plainly of Mij's, a much larger and darker creature, whose fur was short and shiny and the colour of milkless chocolate. These two skins now reposed in my flat, pregnant with possibility and as yet unexamined by competent authority.

I telephoned to the Natural History department of the British Museum, in Cromwell Road, and the same afternoon Mr Robert Hayman arrived at my flat to examine the two skins and the living specimen. There is in the serious zoological world a dead-pan-ness, an unwillingness for committal, that must rival the most cautious of consulting physicians. Hayman was far too competent a zoologist, far too encyclopedic in his knowledge, to have been unaware in those first moments that he was looking at a skin and a living animal from a habitat that made the race quite unfamiliar to him, but he did not betray it. He took such measurements as Mij would permit, examined him closely, peered at his formidable array of teeth, and left bearing the two skins for comparison with museum series.

But in due course, after the slow, precise, painstaking processes of the taxonomic world, Mij's new race was proclaimed. Hayman summoned me to the museum to see the cabinets of otter skins from all over the Asia, where the larger of mine lay, unlabelled and conspicuously differing from any other, in a drawer by itself, but in apposition to its nearest relatives. These, various sub-species of *Lutrogale*, a short-coated otter with a flat under side to the tail, ranged over most of Eastern Asia; according to their geographical race they were of a variety of hues from pale sandy to medium brown, but none had been recorded west of Sind, in India, and none resembled my specimens in colour.

There are very few people, and even fewer amateur zoologists, who stumble upon a sizeable mammal previously unknown to science; in the nursery world of picture-books of birds and beasts the few who had given their own names to species—Steller's Eider and Sea Eagle, Sharpe's Crow, Humboldt's Woolly Monkey, Meinerzthagen's Forest Hog, Ross's Snow Goose, Grant's Gazelle, Père David's Deer —had been surrounded for me with an aura of romance; they were the creators, partaking a little of the deity, who had contributed to the great panorama of bright living creatures in which, unshadowed and uncomplicated by knowledge, my childish fancy wandered. Now, when Hayman suggested that the new otter should bear my name, I experienced a sharp, brief conflict; I felt that it should bear his, for he, not I, had done the work; but something small and shrill from the nursery days was shouting inside me that I could be translated into the hierarchy of my early gods and wear, however perilously, the halo of a creator. ('Can I have it for my own?') we used to ask when we were small. 'For my *very* own?' Here, surely, was an animal of my very own, to bear my name; every animal that looked like it would always bear my name for ever and ever, unless some odious taxonomist of the future, some leveller, some jealous, dusty scribe of the backroom and the skeletons, were to plot against me and plan the destruction of my tiny, living memorial.)

So Mij and all his race became *Lutrogale perspicillata maxwelli*, and though he is now no more, and there is no ostensible proof that there is another living specimen in the world, I had realized a far-off childish fantasy, and there was a Maxwell's otter.

THE LITTLE MILITARY LEARNED HORSE

Joan Selby-Lowndes

On a bright June day in the year 1765, Mr Philip Astley came riding into London on a white horse to start the new adventure of civilian life. The blue regimentals of the sergeant major were packed away in the bundle strapped to the back of his saddle; in his pocket he carried the certificate of six years' loyal service with the dragoons, and the record of his gallantry in battle; hidden inside his coat was a small leather bag that held all his savings; and the horse he was riding was a personal gift from his officer, Sir William Erskine. These were all his worldly goods, and they did not amount to much, but he had youth, ambition and determination. As he trotted past the last milestone at Hyde Park Corner his courage was high.

His plan was to hire a field just outside London, give displays of horsemanship, and start collecting his fortune at once. With this in mind, he made straight for Islington. It was several years since he had last been there, and he found changes at the Three Hats, the former tea garden where Mr Johnson had entertained the public with displays of trick-riding. Johnson had retired with a fortune, and in his place Mr Price now galloped round the arena.

'Things aren't so easy nowadays,' Mr Price told him in the stable yard afterwards as he rubbed down his sweating horses. 'There's too many people in the game.'

Astley found out what he meant when he came across Price's rival, a man called Sampson, who gave displays in a nearby field. Sampson was an old soldier from Lord Ancram's Light Dragoons, and the two men were soon on friendly terms.

'What the public want is novelty,' he told Astley as he stood on his head on the saddle and galloped his horse round a training track. Sampson was a man of ideas. His tricks were new and he was planning to startle the world by introducing his wife as the first female equestrian.

Nearby at Pentonville, Astley discovered yet another competitor in the field. At the Belvedere Tea Gardens Zucker's Little Learned Horse was a great attraction. This was a different style of show, for Zucker's horse had been trained to perform on its own. It lay down and got up to a word of command; carried a handkerchief in its mouth; answered questions by nodding and shaking its head, and even counted by striking the ground with a foreleg.

Astley realized that if he wanted to draw the public he would have to do better than his rivals. With typical energy and thoroughness he set to work, cultivating the friendship of Price and Sampson. He spent many hours in their company, discussing methods of training, watching them at work, and studying their tricks.

With all these important matters filling his mind he was astonished when he suddenly found himself falling in love. Perhaps it was the sight of Mrs Sampson leaping on and off her husband's horses that first gave his thoughts a romantic push in the direction of a young woman he had recently met who was also a skilled horsewoman. For Astley, though, her chief attraction was her hair; a thick pale gold mass piled on her head.

Before the year was out they were married, and on his wedding night Astley discovered that his young bride's hair was even more dramatic than he had dreamed. Unbound it swept the floor. Never had anything so remarkable been seen before. Proudly he boasted of it to everyone he met.

The young couple found rooms and settled near Islington. Astley took work breaking and training horses for a dealer; at the same time he steadily pursued his plan to prepare a display of horsemanship that would combine the best tricks of Sampson and Price with those of

Zucker's Learned Horse. Astley went to the hiding place where he kept his small store of savings, and, telling his wife he was going to buy a horse, set off for Smithfield.

The big horsemarket was thronged with animals of all shapes and sizes. Astley pushed his way through the crowds keeping a tight hand on the money in his pocket and a sharp eye on the livestock offered for sale. He knew exactly what he was looking for.

He found it when he came across a small brown horse called Billy. There was nothing remarkable about him; he was neither handsome nor showy, but he had an engaging air of liveliness that caught Astley's attention. He stared thoughtfully at the sturdy, cheeky young animal, and Billy stared back with bold bright eyes. That decided the matter. Astley approached the owner and the bargaining began.

'That's a genuine horse you've got there,' the dealer told Astley as he finally pocketed his money, wondering whether he ought to have held out for a higher price.

'I shall find that out for myself, soon enough.' Astley walked away leading his new purchase on the end of a rope; he was wondering how much he had been cheated. Neither of them could know that for £5 he had just bought the horse that was to lay the foundation of his fortune and make the name of Astley famous in circus history.

Mrs Astley was not at all impressed when she saw the new arrival in the stable yard. She thought £5 was a lot of money to give for such a small uninteresting-looking animal, and said so. Her husband informed her loftily that outward appearance was of no importance. The only things he looked for were courage and good temper.

'This 'ere animal,' he pointed out to her, 'has eyes bright and resolute, and impudent, that will look at a hobject with a kind of disdain.'

His estimate of Billy's character was perfectly correct. The bold, good-tempered young horse was quick to learn what was wanted of him. Astley soon had him obedient to voice, whip and rein, and started him on dressage and high school work. At the same time he began teaching him some of the tricks he had seen Zucker's horse perform. To his delight he found that Billy was a born actor. He soon learned to lie down and stay on the ground until commanded to rise; and it was not long before he would pick things up in his mouth and carry them about. Astley taught him also to undo his own girths and take off his saddle.

Billy became a great favourite; and whenever Astley went into the stables there would always be an apple or some titbit in his pocket for his bright young pupil.

★   ★   ★   ★

The brassy notes of a trumpet shrilled through the air.

'Walk up! Walk up ladies and gentlemen, and see the amazing exhibition of activity on horseback!'

Passers-by, startled by the stentorian voice, stopped to stare at the splendid figure stationed at the foot of Westminster Bridge. Astley, dressed in full regimentals, sat on his showy white charger distributing handbills.

'That there is the riding school,' he announced, waving his drawn sword at the entire south bank of the river. The people moved on clutching his handbills, and those who could read learned that Mr Astley, late Sergeant Major in His Majesty's Royal Regiment of Light Dragoons, would perform: 'near twenty different attitudes on one, two and three horses, every evening during the summer, Sundays excepted, at his Riding School on Halfpenny Hatch. Doors to be opened at 4, he will mount at 5.'

The grandly styled Riding School was, in fact, a derelict field in the Lambeth Marshes which Astley had hired for the summer. He had chosen this unfashionable corner of the London scene, across the river, because here he was free of rivals. On the other hand, there were no pleasure grounds or tea gardens to bring in the public! Astley himself was to be the sole attraction. He certainly aroused a great deal of curiosity as he paraded each morning at the foot of Westminster Bridge to announce his show. At the end of the week even his powerful voice was feeling the strain, and he was quite hoarse by the time he returned to the field, where his wife was hard at work dragging out the long wooden benches, assisted by a boy who had been engaged to do odd jobs and beat the drum.

'This way, ladies and gentlemen,' Astley bawled, 'one shilling for a seat, sixpence to stand.'

The shillings and sixpences grew heavy in his pocket, and the buzz of voices swelled as the benches filled and the standing people crowded onto the grass behind the roped-off riding arena.

While the crowd waited, they were entertained by the sight of a small boy carrying a large drum, scrambling up to the roof of an old pigeon house in the centre that was to do duty as a bandstand. The rest of the spectators were preparing to see the show free. Astley caught sight of a bunch of grimy inquisitive faces pressed against the cracks in the palings, and directed a blistering fire of sergeant major abuse at them. The faces promptly vanished, only to reappear further along, the moment his back was turned; but Astley had no more time for sentry duty, the show must begin. In the stables, his wife was leading out the first horse.

The boy on the pigeon house began a frenzied beating on his drum as Astley mounted, rode into the ring, and bowed. His powerful voice echoed round the field as he announced his first tricks. There was another roll on the drum, and Astley put his horse at a gallop and stood up on the saddle. The simplest feats came first: he balanced on one leg, then jumped round to face the horse's tail. Working up to a more spectacular display he stood on his head on the saddle. The crowd were silent now, awed by this extraordinary sight, and when they saw him, still upside down, draw a pistol, women covered their ears while the men leaned forward, open-mouthed, waiting for him to break his neck. Astley pressed the trigger. There was a roar and a spurt of flame, but the horse did not falter, and Astley was up on his feet again on the saddle, the smoking pistol still in his hand, acknowledging the applause.

He collected a second horse, and there was a murmur of wonder as the crowd watched him ride them at a gallop round the arena with a foot on each saddle. When he finally put them at a bar, and they sailed over it, jumping neck and neck with their rider standing upright on their backs, enthusiastic applause rang out.

The sweat was running down Astley's face as he slid to the ground, and handed his wife the reins of the two lathered horses. It was now the turn of Little Billy, and he had high hopes of this part of the show.

'Ladies and Gentlemen,' he boomed. 'I now beg leave to introduce for your entertainment the Little Military Learned Horse.' He paused while the crowd gaped at Billy, who stood quietly at his master's side. 'This horse will, in a manner most extraordinary, appear dead.'

At a signal from his master, Billy obligingly lay down, and Astley embarked on a poem that he himself had composed for the occasion. It had needed much head-scratching and pen-chewing to produce these rhymes, for he found it easier to teach Billy to lie down than to write about it.

'My horse lies dead, apparent at your sight.

But I'm the man can set the thing to right,' Astley the poet bawled at the top of his voice, while Billy, obeying the prod of a boot, rolled over on his side and went quite limp.

'Speak when you please, I'm ready to obey,

My faithful horse knows what I want to say.

But first, pray give me leave to move his foot.'

Astley picked up a relaxed foreleg and let it drop in a most realistic manner.

The crowd were deeply impressed.

'That he is dead is quite beyond dispute.

This shows how brutes by heaven were designed

To be in full subjection to mankind.'

Billy lay without moving, and by this time the crowd were almost convinced that he *was* dead. Handkerchiefs began to appear. Astley stood letting the effect sink in until they could bear the suspense no longer and called out to have him brought back to life. He bowed.

'Rise young Bill, and be a little handy

To serve that warlike hero General Granby.'

He was conscious that this was not one of his best rhymes, but it did not matter, for everyone's attention was now fixed on the horse. Little Billy raised his head, looked about him, and then heaved himself up onto his legs. The crowd, vastly relieved, broke into loud applause.

'When you have seen all my Bill's expresst,'

Astley shouted into the uproar,

'My wife, to conclude, performs the rest.'

Billy went through his repertoire of tricks, and finally Mrs Astley made her dramatic appearance standing on the backs of two horses. With her long golden hair floating out behind her, and her long skirts flying around her ankles, she looked like some windborne sprite. In

The astonished crowd saw the Learned Horse count to six with his hoof.

one frail feminine hand, however, she clutched a loaded pistol, which she boldly fired into the air as she galloped past the shilling places.

This was the climax and finish of the show. The boy with the drum slithered down from the pigeon house; the crowd broke up and began to drift out of the field. Astley and his wife sat in the saddle room counting the takings. A satisfying pile of coins lay on the table between them.

'And this is only the beginning.' Astley was already seeing his fortune made. 'As time goes on, it will get better.'

★   ★   ★   ★

As the news of Astley's skill and activities spread, he began to see the first results of all his efforts. People came to Halfpenny Hatch in ever-increasing numbers. At the height of the season he was taking as much as forty guineas a day at the entrance. His faith in his own abilities had been justified.

The first season of the new riding school in the Westminster Bridge Road opened with a bang. This was Mrs Astley beating the drum. Escorted by two men blowing shrill tunes on pipes, she paraded up and down the road followed by Astley and the white charger, complete with trumpet, sword and handbills.

'Walk up! walk up! One shilling for a seat, sixpence standing,' his old cry made itself heard through the clamour of the band. 'Children and servants threepence!'

The combined noise of drum, pipes and the sergeant major's voice attracted a large crowd, who paid their money and went in. This year he was giving them a bigger and better performance. Mrs Astley and Little Billy had learned new tricks. There were other improvements also: Astley had done away with the odd-job boy and the drum, and engaged proper musicians. Even now those two harassed gentlemen, who had been bursting their lungs up and down the road all the morning, were scrambling onto the wooden platform in the middle of the arena, to be a two-man band.

The pattern of the performance was much the same as before. Astley gave his display of 'attitudes' on the saddle, and made his horses leap a bar. After this Little Billy came into the arena to perform the

'Sham Death of Little Military Learned Horse', by now firmly established as a favourite. Then Mrs Astley made her entrance. She went through her tricks with all her old skill and vigour, while their son John, born a few months earlier, slept on peacefully unaware that his mother was risking her neck on the backs of two galloping horses.

'We have only these 'ere two horses to ride,' Astley's booming voice announced. 'So we shall ride together until Mrs Astley chooses to alight at full speed with elegance and ease.' He vaulted up behind her.

'And this time, don't push me,' she hissed over her shoulder at him as they stood together on the saddles, smiling to the crowd, while the white charger and his stable companion cantered placidly round the ride.

'Now! Jump!' Astley nudged her as they circled towards the shilling seats for the second time.

'Mind your own business.' She stamped on his foot, nearly overbalanced, and then deliberately waited until they were passing the sixpenny places.

Striking a graceful attitude, which was the signal for a roll on the drum, she gritted her teeth and jumped to the ground. The well-trained horses carried Astley out of the arena while she picked up her skirts and acknowledged the applause with a graceful curtsey and a modest smile. The reckoning would come later. Astley scowled furiously at her as she tripped jauntily past him, while he led Little Billy into the arena for his second appearance.

He had spent many patient hours teaching his horse new tricks. Little Billy could now nod and shake his head to order. Obeying a private system of signals he followed Astley round the arena sorting out ladies from gentlemen to the giggling delight of the crowd.

Astley then announced that his Learned Horse would tell the time; and the astonished crowd saw Billy strike six o'clock on the ground with his hoof while Astley's loud running commentary drowned the small click of thumb and finger nail which was the signal for each stroke. After this, he proceeded to go lame and hobbled about on three legs.

'My horse is sick,' Astley shouted, and gave Billy the signal to shake his head. 'He has a pain in his head,' he explained, and went on, in a burst of rhyme, to tell Billy that, although he was sick, he must go and fight for the Spaniards. But Billy, who had been taught to be a loyal British horse, promptly grew worse. He lay down and died, and remained dead until the last lines of the poem, when Astley told him he must go and fight for England with General Eliott's Dragoons. This at once brought Billy to life again. He got onto his feet, and, obeying another click, fired off a pistol with his hoof to the cheering delight of the crowd.

Little Billy's clever tricks were a great attraction. The fame of the Little Military Learned Horse spread, and people from all over London began flocking to the Westminster Bridge Road to see him.

In Pentonville, Zucker's Little Learned Horse might gnash his teeth in rage, for whatever he did the Little Learned Military Horse in Lambeth went one better. When the Learned Horse carried a loaded tea tray about, the Military Learned Horse picked a kettle of boiling water from the fire, in his mouth, to make the tea which he then served on a tray.

Astley was also quick to see the possibilities in other types of entertainment. For some time he had had his eye on another place of amusement in Islington that seemed to have discovered the secret of permanent popularity.

For nearly a hundred years Sadler's Wells had been attracting people. They had come first in the reign of King Charles to drink the waters of its famous wells; later to drink tea and listen to music. Now the place had been turned into a theatre, and people went there to be entertained by clowns, singers, tumblers and acrobats. This gave Astley the idea of adding other attractions to his own show.

Mrs Astley's voice became shrill when she discovered that he was also planning to spend all their profits on improvements to the showground.

'You have a child to support, so how can you risk all our hard-earned money on this place,' she said angrily. At that moment she hated the place, and looked with disgust at the trail of disorder; the jumbled benches, the trampled grass strewn with orange-peel and litter.

'It is getting late, let us go to bed.' Astley took his wife's arm. But she had not finished yet.

'What improvements are you planning?' she persisted.

'Covered seats for everyone,' his hand circled the whole arena. 'A proper entrance, stabling, and a gallery for the nobility.' He was determined to attract society to his establishment. 'With proper shelter we can give the performance even if there is a shower of rain.'

'So the people can sit and watch us getting soaked to the skin, risking our necks on slippery saddles! You would do better to spend the money putting the shelter over our heads,' she added sarcastically.

Astley did not reply. He looked up at the clear sky over the open field, and perhaps it was his wife's angry words that first gave him the vision of the day when he would build a roof to span the whole of his riding school, turning it into one great amphitheatre: Astley's Amphitheatre!

★　　　★　　　★　　　★

Over the next twenty years, despite keen competition from his rivals, Astley went from strength to strength. In 1779 he opened Astley's Amphitheatre Riding-House, the first modern circus building in the world. He took his show on tour in Europe, and in 1785 opened the first circus in Paris, the *Amphitheatre Anglaise*. In 1786 the London amphitheatre was completely refurbished, and renamed The Royal Grove, and the pattern of the next few years was set. Winters in Paris, summers in England, with John managing the Royal Grove, and Philip travelling and building. He even crossed the Irish Channel to establish Astley's Amphitheatre in Dublin.

In the end he left a trail of seventeen Amphitheatres strung across the provinces. These, with the establishments in London and Paris, made a grand total of nineteen amphitheatres built with the money, brains and energy of one man. It earned him the nickname of Amphi-Philip. No one, however, dared to use it to his face, for Astley would not tolerate such lack of respect. His success had made him very grand.

★　　　★　　　★　　　★

The French Revolution of 1789 forced him to give up the Paris building, and then, in 1793, a series of events took place that shocked and outraged the whole of England. On 21 January, King Louis XVI was guillotined in Paris. A month later the aggressive new Republic of France, announcing that it would carry its revolutionary ideas into other countries, invaded Belgium and declared war on Holland and England.

The English, who had at first cheered and approved of the French people's gallant struggle for freedom, were furious and resentful. The Duke of York immediately set about raising an army. In London the streets began to echo to the drums of the recruiting sergeants and to the tramp of marching feet. These stirring military sounds reached Astley's ears and made him fret like an old war horse, and when he saw the proud uniforms and regimental colours parading through the city he could bear it no longer. He shook off his fifty years, and hurried away to offer his services to his King and country.

There were many things to arrange before he left. A soldier going on a campaign might be away a long time. He decided to give his son a seven-year lease on the amphitheatre.

In the middle of the activity Abraham Saunders arrived one day to see Astley and beg a special favour. Astley had known Saunders for many years. He had run a prosperous place of entertainment in Whitechapel. Then a run of bad luck had hit him. First a fire had completely destroyed his theatre, and then all his horses and his company had been drowned in the Irish Channel. Saunders had been struggling to build up his fortunes ever since, and Astley felt sorry for him. He was ready to help with money, but that was not what Saunders wanted. He was asking to borrow the Little Military Learned Horse.

'With that little horse of yours I can draw in the public,' Saunders pleaded. 'It'll turn the tide in my favour again.'

Astley was deeply distressed. He offered Saunders the choice of any other horse in his stable, but it seemed that Little Billy with his famous reputation was the only one who would do.

'You shall have him back safe and sound within a week,' Saunders promised. So, reluctantly, Astley allowed Little Billy to be taken out of his stall and led away.

'I don't like it, Johnny.' He shook his head unhappily. 'I don't like it at all.' Staring at the empty stall he could not shake off his feeling of uneasiness.

A week passed with no further news of Billy. Astley, arriving home at the end of the day, handed over his horse to an ostler and strode into the stables where John was in conference with Mr Smith, their chief rough rider.

'Is he back?' This was Astley's regular question the moment he got in.

'No, Father,' John replied. This had become a regular answer, but this time there was a difference. Astley frowned, aware suddenly of a strange tense silence that was spreading through the place like a chill wind.

'What's the matter?' he challenged. 'You have had news of my horse? Come now, out with it,'

'I'm afraid, Father, that Billy has been lost.' John paused, waiting for an outburst of violence. Instead he saw his father stagger, and reach out to grip a stall post.

'What do you mean?' The loud voice was strangely subdued.

'It appears that Saunders was heavily in debt,' John told him. 'Only three days after you saw him he was seized by his creditors and thrown into prison. They held a sale of all his possessions, including the horses. Billy was sold along with the rest.'

Astley turned abruptly, and without saying a word walked out of the stables.

'The old man's taken it hard,' Smith shook his head.

'I've never seen him like that before,' said John in a quiet voice. They were both silent, wondering if it had been their imagination, or a trick of the candlelight, or had they really seen old Astley's eyes fill with tears.

★　　　★　　　★　　　★

It was a warm sunlit afternoon in September. Two of Astley's equestrian performers were strolling through a cobbled street in the East End of London on their way back to the Amphitheatre for the evening performance. A church clock struck.

'That's the half-hour, Tom.' One of the men quickened his pace.

'It's too warm to hurry,' the other yawned. At that moment he would gladly have exchanged his strenuous life in the riding arena for the placid existence of the old men he saw sitting in their doorways puffing at long clay pipes. Even this dingy East End street looked pleasant enough with that sunlight slanting down between the huddled houses; shining on the cobbles where the sparrows pecked; warming the back of an old brown horse dozing in the shafts of a rickety cart. Tom gave the horse a casual glance, and then suddenly he stopped, and stood staring.

'What's the matter with you?' The other pulled impatiently at his arm.

'I say, Jack, I'm a Dutchman if that ain't our Billy.'

'Impossible,' said Jack. It was three years since Billy had been given up as lost, and he had almost forgotten what the little horse looked like.

'I tell you it is.' Tom shook himself free and strode across the street. There was something about this sad-looking brown horse in its shabby harness that convinced him it was indeed their Billy.

'It is his size and colour,' Jack admitted as he had a closer look. 'But how can we be certain?'

'I'll try him.' Tom knew the signals Astley used for some of Billy's tricks. He began to click the nails of his thumb and forefinger. In the quiet street the sound carried clearly. The horse suddenly jerked up his head. They saw him prick his ears, and then, as though obeying some half-forgotten instinct, he arched his neck and began to caper.

'It is him! It's our Billy!' Both men rushed forward, and the next moment the horse was rubbing his head against them.

'He remembers us.' Tom had his arms round Billy's neck.

'Think of the old man's face when we tell him,' said Jack.

'When he sees him, you mean.' Tom plunged his hands in his pockets to discover how much money he had about him. 'We must find his owner without delay.'

It was not difficult. They found Billy's owner in the nearest pub sitting behind a large tankard of ale. He was astonished when he learned that these two prosperous-looking men were interested in buying his old horse, but he was always ready to make a bargain, and so a price was agreed upon and the money paid. The three of them then went out together.

'He's a monstrous good-tempered creature,' the man told them as he took off Billy's harness, 'but he's got such odd antics we call him the Mountebank.' He slipped a rope halter over Billy's head. 'There you are gentlemen.' He handed over their bargain, and the two men led him triumphantly away.

Astley was changing into his best boots ready for the evening performance when Mrs Connell, the housekeeper, tapped on the door.

'There's two men downstairs to see you, sir.'

'I haven't time to see anyone,' Astley growled. 'What do they want?'

'It's a very important matter, sir,' she insisted. 'I think you should go.'

Astley didn't see the twinkle in her eyes. Grumbling and grunting he pulled on his boots and stumped away.

'You'll find them outside in the road,' she called over the banisters.

'Eh? Why don't they come in?'

Mrs Connell did not reply. She was hurrying to the landing window to watch the scene. Astley thumped into the hall. The front door stood wide open. Through it he caught sight of two of his performers standing in the road. He scowled. Someone was playing a joke.

'What does this mean?' He strode out of the house ready to blast the smiles off the men's faces. 'What are you . . .' he broke off staring, for they had led forward a small brown horse.

'We've found him,' they said simply.

'Billy!' At the sound of that well known voice calling his name the horse pricked up his ears and whickered. The next moment Astley was beside him and Billy was rubbing his head against his master and nuzzling at his pocket as though he had never been away. Astley's hand shook as he fondled his old favourite, and this time there was no mistaking the tears in his eyes. He listened to the men tell how they had found him, then swiftly he ran his hand over the horse's legs and body to reassure himself that Billy was fit and well.

'Wherever he has been these past three years they've taken good care of him,' was Astley's verdict, and pulling out a handkerchief he blew his nose loudly. He was deeply moved. All his fortunes were bound up with the life of this little horse. Billy had been lost, and fire had destroyed his theatre. Now the new Royal Amphitheatre had opened, and Billy had miraculously returned to ensure its success.

'Never again does this 'ere horse go out of my stables,' Astley declared, and he himself led Billy to the stall that was to be his home for the rest of his life.

'I shall have to see if he's forgotten his tricks,' Astley said. Billy hadn't. Twenty years' training had stamped itself indelibly on his memory. He responded at once to all his master's signals. The very next evening Astley announced that by special request, the Little Military Learned Horse would appear, and into the lighted arena trotted the small brown horse that two days before had been hauling a cart through the east end streets of London. The public had not forgotten their old favourite. Billy went through his tricks with all his usual lively assurance, and Astley, watching him take off his saddle, wash his feet in a pail of water, lift a boiling kettle in his mouth and play the waiter, felt a surge of pride and a deep reassurance. Billy was back, and from now on good fortune would go with them.

THE HUNTING OF THE WHITE WHALE

Herman Melville

Moby Dick, Herman Melville's extraordinary, rich and poetic novel of the sea, tells the story of Captain Ahab's obsession with the great white whale who was responsible for the loss of his leg. Through the South Seas the Pequod and her crew search for Moby Dick. Captain Ahab nails to the ship's mast a gold doubloon, which will be given to the man who first spies the white whale. At last Moby Dick is sighted by the Captain himself, and a chase begins.

That night, in the mid-watch, when the old man—as his wont at intervals—stepped forth from the scuttle in which he leaned, and went to his pivot-hole, he suddenly thrust out his face fiercely, snuffing up the sea air as a sagacious ship's dog will, in drawing nigh to some barbarous isle. He declared that a whale must be near. Soon that peculiar odour, sometimes to a great distance given forth by the living Sperm Whale, was palpable to all the watch nor was any mariner surprised when, after inspecting the compass, and then the dog-vane, and then ascertaining the precise bearing of the odour as nearly as possible, Ahab rapidly ordered the ship's course to be slightly altered, and the sail to be shortened.

The acute policy dictating these movements was sufficiently vindicated at daybreak by the sight of a long sleek on the sea directly and lengthwise ahead, smooth as oil, and resembling in the pleated watery wrinkles bordering it, the polished metallic-like marks of some swift tide-rip, at the mouth of a deep, rapid stream.

'Man the mastheads! Call all hands!'

Thundering with the butts of three clubbed handspikes on the forecastle deck, Daggoo, the negro harpooner, roused the sleepers with such judgment claps that they seemed to exhale from the scuttle, so instantaneously did they appear with their clothes in their hands.

'What d'ye see?' cried Ahab, flattening his face to the sky.

'Nothing, nothing, sir!' was the sound hailing down in reply.

'T'gallant-sails! stunsails alow and aloft, and on both sides!'

All sail being set, he now cast loose the life-line, reserved for swaying him to the mainroyal masthead; and in a few moments they were hoisting him thither, when, while but two-thirds of the way aloft, and while peering ahead through the horizontal vacancy between the maintopsail and topgallant-sail, he raised a gull-like cry in the air. 'There she blows!—there she blows! A hump like a snowhill! It is Moby Dick!'

Fired by the cry which seemed simultaneously taken up by the three lookouts, the men on deck rushed to the rigging to behold the famous whale they had so long been pursuing. Ahab had now gained his final perch, some feet above the other lookouts, Tashtego, the Red Indian harpooner, standing just beneath him on the cap of the top-gallant-mast, so that his head was almost on a level with Ahab's heel. From this height the whale was now seen some mile or so ahead, at every roll of the sea revealing his high sparkling hump, and regularly jetting his silent spout into the air. To the credulous mariners it seemed the same silent spout they had so long ago beheld in the moonlit Atlantic and Indian Oceans.

'And did none of ye see it before?' cried Ahab, hailing the perched men all around him.

'I saw him almost that same instant, sir, that Captain Ahab did, and I cried out,' said Tashtego.

'Not the same instant; not the same—no, the doubloon is mine, Fate reserved the doubloon for me. *I* only; none of ye could have raised the White Whale first. There she blows! there she blows!—there she blows! There again!—there again!' he cried, in long-drawn, lingering, methodic tones, attuned to the gradual prolongings of the whale's visible jets. 'He's going to sound! In stunsails! Down top-gallant-sails! Stand by three boats. Mr Starbuck, remember, stay on board, and keep the ship. Helm there! Luff, luff a point! So; steady, man, steady!

There go flukes! No, no; only black water! All ready the boats there? Stand by, stand by! Lower me, Mr Starbuck; lower, lower,—quick, quicker!' and he slid through the air to the deck.

'He is heading straight to leeward, sir,' cried Stubb, the second mate; 'right away from us; cannot have seen the ship yet.'

'Be dumb, man! Stand by the braces! Hard down the helm!—brace up! Shiver her!—shiver her! So; well that! Boats, boats!'

Soon all the boats but Starbuck's were dropped; all the boat-sails set—all the paddles plying; with rippling swiftness, shooting to leeward; and Ahab heading the onset. A pale, death-glimmer lit up the sunken eyes of Fedallah, the Indian; a hideous motion gnawed his mouth.

Like noiseless nautilus shells, their light prows sped through the sea; but only slowly they neared the foe. As they neared him, the ocean grew still more smooth; seemed drawing a carpet over its waves; seemed a noon-meadow, so serenely it spread. At length the breathless hunter came so nigh his seemingly unsuspecting prey, that his entire dazzling hump was distinctly visible, sliding along the sea as if an isolated thing, and continually set in a revolving ring of finest, fleecy, greenish foam. He saw the vast involved wrinkles of the slightly projecting head beyond. Before it, far out on the soft Turkish-rugged waters, went the glistening white shadow from his broad, milky forehead, a musical rippling playfully accompanying the shade; and behind, the blue waters interchangeably flowed over into the moving valley of his steady wake; and on either hand bright bubbles arose and danced by his side. But these were broken again by the light toes of hundreds of gay fowl softly feathering the sea, alternate with their fitful flight; and like to some flagstaff rising from the painted hull of an argosy, the tall but shattered pole of a recent lance projected from the white whale's back; and at intervals one of the cloud of soft-toed fowls hovering, and to and fro skimming like a canopy over the fish, silently perched and rocked on this pole, the long tail feathers streaming like pennons.

A gentle joyousness—a mighty mildness of repose in swiftness, invested the gliding whale. Not the white bull Jupiter swimming away with ravished Europa clinging to his graceful horns; his lovely, leering eyes sideways intent upon the maid; with smooth bewitching fleetness, rippling straight for the nuptial bower in Crete; not Jove did surpass the glorified White Whale as he so divinely swam.

On each soft side—coincident with the parted swell, that but once laving him, then flowed so wide way—on each bright side, the whale shed off enticings. No wonder there had been some among the hunters who namelessly transported and allured by all this serenity, had ventured to assail it; but had fatally found that quietude but the vesture of tornadoes. Yet calm, enticing calm, oh, whale! thou glidest on, to all who for the first time eye thee, no matter how many in that same way thou may'st have bejuggled and destroyed before.

And thus, through the serene tranquillities of the tropical sea, among waves whose hand-clappings were suspended by exceeding rapture, Moby Dick moved on, still withholding from sight the full terrors of his submerged trunk, entirely hiding the wretched hideousness of his jaw. But soon the fore part of him slowly rose from the water; for an instant his whole marbleized body formed a high arch, like Virginia's Natural Bridge, and warningly waving his bannered flukes in the air, the grand god revealed himself, sounded, and went out of sight. Hoveringly halting, and dipping on the wing, the white sea-fowls longingly lingered over the agitated pool that he left.

With oars apeak, and paddles down, the sheets of their sails adrift, the three boats now stilly floated, awaiting Moby Dick's reappearance.

'An hour,' said Ahab, standing rooted in his boat's stern, and he gazed beyond the whale's place, towards the dim blue spaces and wide wooing vacancies to leeward. It was only an instant; for again his eyes seemed whirling round in his head as he swept the watery circle. The breeze now freshened; the sea began to swell.

'The birds!—the birds!' cried Tashtego.

In long Indian file, as when herons take wing, the white birds were now all flying towards Ahab's boat; and when within a few yards began fluttering over the water there, wheeling round and round, with joyous, expectant cries. Their vision was keener than man's; Ahab could discover no sign in the sea. But suddenly as he peered down and down into its depths, he profoundly saw a white living spot no bigger than a white weasel, with wonderful celerity uprising, and magnifying as it rose, till it turned, and then there were plainly revealed two long crooked rows of white, glistening teeth, floating up from the undiscoverable bottom. It was Moby Dick's open mouth and scrolled jaw; his vast, shadowed bulk still half blending with the blue of the sea. The glittering mouth yawned beneath the boat like an open-doored marble tomb; and giving one sidelong sweep with his steering oar, Ahab whirled the craft aside from this tremendous apparition. Then, calling upon Fedellah to change places with him, went forward to the bows, and seizing Perth's harpoon, commanded his crew to grasp their oars and stand by to stern.

Now, by reason of this timely spinning round the boat upon its axis, its bow, by anticipation, was made to face the whale's head while yet under water. But as if perceiving this stratagem, Moby Dick, with that malicious intelligence ascribed to him, sidelingly transplanted himself, as it were, in an instant, shooting his plaited head lengthwise beneath the boat.

Through and through; through every plank and each rib, it thrilled for an instant, the whale obliquely lying on its back, in the manner of a biting shark, slowly and feelingly taking its bows full within his mouth, so that the long, narrow, scrolled lower jaw curled high up into the open air, and one of the teeth caught in a rowlock. The bluish pearl-white of the inside of the jaw was within six inches of Ahab's head, and reached higher than that. In this attitude the White Whale now shook the slight cedar as a mildly cruel cat her mouse. With unastonished eyes Fedallah gazed, and crossed his arms; but the tiger-yellow crew were tumbling over each other's heads to gain the utter-most stern.

And now, while both elastic gunwales were springing in and out, as the whale dallied with the doomed craft in this devilish way; and from his body being submerged beneath the boat, he could not be darted at from the bows, for the bows were almost inside of him, as it were; and while the other boats involuntarily paused, as before a quick crisis impossible to withstand, then it was that monomaniac Ahab, furious with this tantalising vicinity of his foe, which placed him all alive and helpless in the very jaws he hated; frenzied with all this, he seized the long bone with his naked hands, and wildly strove to wrench it from its gripe. As now he thus vainly strove, the jaw slipped from him; the frail gunwales bent in, collapsed, and snapped, as both jaws, like an enormous shears, sliding further aft, bit the craft completely in twain, and locked themselves fast again in the sea, midway between the two floating wrecks. These floated aside, the broken ends drooping, the crew at the stern-wreck clinging to the gunwales, and striving to hold fast to the oars to lash them across.

At that preluding moment, ere the boat was yet snapped, Ahab, the first to perceive the whale's intent, by the crafty upraising of his head, a movement that loosed his hold for the time; at that moment his hand had made one final effort to push the boat out of the bite. But only slipping further into the whale's mouth, and tilting over sideways as it slipped, the boat had shaken off his hold on the jaw; spilled him out of it, as he leaned to the push; and so he fell flat-faced upon the sea.

Ripplingly withdrawing from his prey, Moby Dick now lay at a little distance, vertically thrusting his oblong white head up and down in the billows; and at the same time slowly revolving his whole spindled body; so that when his vast wrinkled forehead rose—some twenty or more feet out of the water—the now rising swells, with all their con-fluent waves, dazzling broke against it; vindictively tossing their shivered spray still higher into the air. So, in a gale, the but half baffled Channel billows only recoil from the base of the Eddystone, triumphantly to overleap its summit with their scud.

But soon resuming his horizontal attitude, Moby Dick swam swiftly round and round the wrecked crew; sideways churning the water in his vengeful wake, as if lashing himself up to still another more deadly assault. The sight of the splintered boat seemed to madden him, as the blood of grapes and mulberries cast before Antiochus's elephants in the book of Maccabees. Meanwhile Ahab half smothered in the foam of the whale's insolent tail, and too much of a cripple to swim,—though he could still keep afloat, even in the heart of such a whirlpool as that; helpless Ahab's head was seen, like a tossed bubble which the least chance shock might burst. From the boat's fragmentary stern, Fedallah incuriously and mildly eyed him; the clinging crew, at the other drifting end, could not succour him; more than enough was it for them to look to themselves. For so revolvingly appalling was the White Whale's aspect, and so planetarily swift the ever-contracting circles he made, that he seemed horizontally swooping upon them. And though the other boats, unharmed, still hovered hard by, still they dared not

He raised his pale, bleached body and towered menacingly over us.

pull into the eddy to strike, lest that should be the signal for the instant destruction of the jeopardized castaways, Ahab and all; nor in that case could they themselves hope to escape. With straining eyes, then, they remained on the outer edge of the direful zone, whose centre had now become the old man's head.

Meantime, from the beginning all this had been descried from the ship's mastheads; and squaring her yards, she had borne down upon the scene; and was now so nigh, that Ahab in the water hailed her;—'Sail on the'—but that moment a breaking sea dashed on him from Moby Dick, and whelmed him for the time. But struggling out of it again, and chancing to rise on a towering crest, he shouted,—'Sail on the whale!—Drive him off!'

The *Pequod's* prows were pointed; and breaking up the charmed circle, she effectually parted the White Whale from his victim. As he suddenly swam off, the boats flew to the rescue.

Dragged into Stubb's boat with bloodshot, blinded eyes, the white brine caking in his wrinkles; the long tension of Ahab's bodily strength did crack, and helplessly he yielded to his body's doom: for a time, lying all crushed in the bottom of Stubb's boat, like one trodden under foot of herds of elephants. Far inland, nameless wails came from him, as desolate sounds from out ravines.

But this intensity of his physical prostration did but so much the more abbreviate it. In an instant's compass, great hearts sometimes condense to one deep pang, the sum-total of those shallow pains kindly diffused through feebler men's whole lives. And so, such hearts, though summary in each one suffering; still, if the gods decree it, in their lifetime aggregate a whole age of woe, wholly made up of instantaneous intensities; for even in their pointless centres, those noble natures contain the entire circumferences of inferior souls.

'The harpoon,' said Ahab, half-way rising, and draggingly leaning on one bended arm—'it is safe?'

'Aye, sir, for it was not darted; this is it,' said Stubb, showing it.

'Lay it before me;—any missing men?'

'One, two, three, four, five;—there were five oars, sir and here are five men.'

'That's good.—Help me, man; I wish to stand. So, so, I see him! there! there! going to leeward still; what a leaping spout!—Hands off from me! The eternal sap runs up in Ahab's bones again! Set the sail; out oars; the helm!'

It is often the case that when a boat is stove, its crew, being picked up by another boat, help to work that second boat; and the chase is thus continued with what is called double-banked oars. It was thus now. But the added power of the boat did not equal the added power of the whale, for he seemed to have treble-banked his every fin; swimming with a velocity which plainly showed, that if now, under these circumstances, pushed on, the chase would prove an indefinitely prolonged, if not a hopeless one; nor could any crew endure for so long a period, such an unintermitted, intense straining at the oar; a thing barely tolerable only in some one brief vicissitude. The ship itself, then, as it sometimes happens, offered the most promising intermediate means of overtaking the chase. Accordingly, the boats now made for her, and were soon swayed up to their cranes—the two parts of the wrecked boat having been previously secured by her—and then hoisting everything to her side, and stacking her canvas high up, and sideways outstretching it with stunsails, like the double-jointed wings of an albatross; the *Pequod* bore down on the leeward wake of Moby Dick. At the well-known, methodic intervals, the whale's glittering spout was regularly announced from the manned mastheads; and when he would be reported as just gone down, Ahab would take the time, and then pacing the deck, binnacle-watch in hand, so soon as the last second of the allotted hour expired, his voice was heard.— 'Whose is the doubloon now? D'ye see him?' and if the reply was, 'No, sir!' straightway he commanded them to lift him to his perch. In this way the day wore on; Ahab, now aloft and motionless; anon, unrestingly pacing the planks.

As he was thus walking, uttering no sound, except to hail the men aloft, or to bid them hoist a sail still higher, or to spread one to a still greater breadth—thus to and fro pacing, beneath his slouched hat, at every turn he passed his own wrecked boat, which had been dropped upon the quarter-deck, and lay there reversed; broken bow to shattered stern. At last he paused before it; and as in an already over-clouded sky fresh troops of clouds will sometimes sail across, so over the old man's face there now stole some such added gloom as this.

The day was nearly done; only the hem of his golden robe was rustling. Soon, it was almost dark, but the look-out men still remained unset.

'Can't see the spout now, sir;—too dark'—cried a voice from the air.

'How heading when last seen?'

'As before, sir,—straight to leeward.'

'Good! he will travel slower now 'tis night. Down royals and top-gallant stunsails, Mr Starbuck. We must not run over him before morning; he's making a passage now, and may heave-to a while. Helm there! keep her full before the wind!—Aloft! come down!—Mr Stubb, send a fresh hand to the foremast head, and see it manned till morning.'—Then advancing towards the doubloon in the mainmast—'Men, this gold is mine, for I earned it; but I shall let it abide here till the White Whale is dead; and then, whosoever of ye first raises him, upon the day he shall be killed, this gold is that man's; and if on that day I shall again raise him, then, ten times its sum shall be divided among all of ye! Away now!—the deck is thine, sir.'

And so saying, he placed himself half-way within the scuttle, and slouching his hat, stood there till dawn, except when at intervals rousing himself to see how the night wore on.

A WHITE HORSE WITH WINGS

Anthea Davies

In this re-telling of.the ancient Greek myth the hero, Bellerophon, has been ordered by the king.to kill the Chimaera, a monster which has been ravaging the land. He seeks out the beautiful winged horse Pegasus, and tames him with a magic bridle. Together they spend a week training for the battle with the monster, using a cabbage stuck on a stake for target practice.

In the cool of the day Bellerophon waded out into the bay and rescued the target, and moved it on to a ledge below which the slabs of rock jutted out like fangs. He lit his fire, taking an armful of smelly seaweed up there on Pegasus's back, which annoyed the horse considerably. Then they flew at the target from about three, four and five hundred feet in succession, and cut off its cabbage head all three times. Each dive was perfect.

That was the end of the training, and Pegasus was so pleased with himself that he did one of his most hair-raising tricks—scrambling up the steep side of the inlet on his feet, with the loose rocks shifting and toppling as he gripped them, only opening his wings when he slipped down, or fell backwards from the overhanging boulders.

'Absurd creature,' said Bellerophon happily. 'Now fly along and play while I sharpen the sword, and then we'll both have an early night.'

Half an hour later he found himself sitting on the cliff-edge shouting: 'Pegasus! Bedtime!' to the horse weaving in the air like a bat. Pegasus at once went and hid in a cloud, and Bellerophon lay back on the dewy grass and laughed.

'You make me feel such a fool sometimes,' he chuckled. Pegasus finally flew down to him, pretending to try to knock him off the cliff.

Next morning before daybreak Bellerophon schooled Pegasus for the last time on the shore. The tide was coming in, and Pegasus minced along with his head tucked demurely in and his ears nicely forward, swishing his tail and giving little bucks and snorts. Once he raised his wings and clapped them, and shook them into place again, like a game little merlin on the falconer's wrist.

'Up,' said Bellerophon, eventually, and the horse took off as lightly as if he hadn't been working harder during the past week than he had at any time in his life since he was a fledgling.

They flew inland, towards the east. The journey took two days. On the morning of the third day they drew near to a lonely mountain that reared up in the eye of the rising sun, above a richly cultivated plain. On the ground below them they saw as they flew several large burnt patches, some still smoking, and a smouldering farmhouse where grimfaced men and women were trying to save their belongings from the flames. As Pegasus's shadow fell across them they scattered like sparrows from a hawk, but Bellerophon coaxed the horse down to the fire and looked in at all the windows to make sure there was no one trapped inside.

'Did the Chimaera do this?' he called, and the people came out of cover, staring and dazed, and answered that he had, and that he had also carried off a child. They were too griefstricken to be amazed at the winged horse. They told Bellerophon that the monster was three times as big as Pegasus, with enormous wings of naked skin. They did not hold out much hope, but they cheered the horse and rider revengefully and hoarsely on their way. Bellerophon thought he would never forget their smoke-blackened faces.

'Only people who have seen the Chimaera will take *you* for granted also,' he said to Pegasus as they flew on. 'But I also have seen the monster—in my dreams. Oh, horrible!'

They went over the last village, which was just waking up, so that the cocks crowed at Pegasus from the housetops and the beasts, brought into the streets every night for safety, stamped and jostled each other, and started the dogs barking.

Beyond that was a great swath of desolate and darkened ground.

Then they flew up to the inaccessible cave in the mountain that only wings could reach, where the monster had its den. Bellerophon had known that he could have no hope of killing the monster unless he too had wings, and could take it unawares in the place where it thought it was unassailable. To this purpose he had had the magic bridle made, and then sought for the legendary Pegasus over half the kingdom.

He had hoped that the Chimaera would be lying gorged and half-sleeping in the cave-mouth, but when Pegasus swayed past the dark hole as silently as an owl, there was nothing to be seen. However, the reek of the monster's fumes blew out of the opening, and Bellerophon, his heart drumming, took a deep breath and shouted:

'Come on, Chimaera, let's see you then!'

On the heels of his shout Pegasus neighed fiercely. The tunnel echoed, and then there was silence, while Pegasus hovered, waiting.

'It can't be as big as they said, unless it's long and thin,' said Bellerophon, shakily, 'or it'd never get in through that crevice.'

They heard suddenly the scraping of claws and hoofs on rock, and the Chimaera slowly appeared. It was no bigger than Pegasus, and with a shorter spread of wing. It had three deformed heads, those of a lion, a goat and a serpent. Its forefeet were those of a lion, and its hindfeet those of a goat, and its body was long and scaly with a sinuous tail. It breathed flame from its six nostrils. It looked grotesque, ridiculous even, with all the unreasonable horror of a nightmare. Bellerophon, who had once or twice had the tears brought to his eyes by Pegasus's unfathomable beauty, had the crazy feeling that if he laughed long enough at this incomprehensible chaos it would vanish into nothing.

There could be no mistaking the malice in the Chimaera's three pairs of eyes as its heads stopped squabbling and slavering over a mangled hand, and turned their brooding regard on Bellerophon and Pegasus. Pegasus stared with enormous eyes and ears tensely pricked, and then spun round as speedily as a dragonfly to get out of range. The monster threatened them with jets of fire.

'We can outfly it, at least,' said Bellerophon, keeping his voice calm and practical, and measuring the ungainly body with his eye. 'But we must tempt it to the edge of the opening, or it'll dodge into the cave every time we attack. Let's tease it a bit.'

144

The monster breathed jets of fire at Bellerophon and Pegasus.

By now Pegasus was quaking and sweating, and each time he was set at the cave-mouth he sheered off-course long before the shooting flames could touch him, while Bellerophon menaced the Chimaera with his sword. But the monster stayed well within its lair, crouched to strike.

'I know,' said Bellerophon at last, and sent Pegasus scrabbling up the side of the mountain above the cave. The horse went willingly enough, loosening the scree with his hoofs as Bellerophon had intended, and sending it tumbling and ringing down the slope. Before they reached the mountain top the Chimaera had been forced out of its den, for the noise not only brought it to the edge of the cliff-face to glare wrathfully up at its enemies, but the sliding shale lodged itself across the cave-mouth and blocked it up, with a great commotion of dust and flying chips. In fact, the Chimaera narrowly missed being trapped inside. As it was, it was caught by the tail for nearly a minute, and had to burrow with its talons to get free.

But although Bellerophon's plan had succeeded far better than he could have hoped, he and Pegasus did not take advantage of the minute's grace they might have had. They were at the top of the mountain, and Pegasus, his head up and laid sidelong into his neck, his ears flattened, his eyes showing bloodshot, and his heels anchored like crowbars, was refusing to go down again. At each attempt Bellerophon made to fly him, he half-opened his wings and then jibbed, backing away from the edge. It was evident that had it not been for his love for Bellerophon he would have flown away altogether.

After a time Bellerophon got off his back, and rubbed the horse's throat and shoulders while he thought. The hide was dank and chill. Pegasus hung his head distressfully over his rider's bent back. Bellerophon wound his arm over Pegasus's neck, and leant forward to look over the steep drop to the cave.

'He's out there all right.' He straightened up. 'All right, Pegasus, my beauty, you've brought me far enough. You stay here and I'll climb down the way you came up, and see if I can take him unawares.'

This was complete nonsense, and he knew it, and he dropped his voice despairingly at the end in spite of himself.

He kissed the horse's face between the eyes, and then let himself down over the edge of the precipice, before he could start to feel as panic-stricken as Pegasus.

Immediately, his feet began to slip, and then his handholds gave way. As he lost his grip and went bumping down his held breath came out in a scream, and Pegasus neighed furiously from above him. The monster answered with a bellow.

Then Pegasus leapt over the cliff after Bellerophon, and caught the swordbelt in his teeth. Bellerophon, winded and badly grazed, hauled himself up as best he could with Pegasus's help, while the horse's wings lashed round him and his steamy breath blew into his hair.

Pegasus dumped him at the top, and waited impatiently for him to recover himself. Bellerophon stopped gasping, and adjusted the swordbelt over his chafed belly. Then he eyed the horse that loomed over him and grinned. Pegasus's eyes were still huge with fright, but his ears were flicking to and fro naturally, and his neck was curved so that the skin puckered into wrinkles behind his cheek. He scraped the ground with his forefeet and fluttered his wings nervously but urgently. Not for nothing had Bellerophon praised his courage.

Bellerophon climbed on his back, and the horse sailed unhesitatingly out over the Chimaera's vantage point. Bellerophon drew his sword with a flash in the sun. The monster gathered itself together to pounce. Pegasus circled upwards and then idled, turning in the light wind and choosing his moment. Not for nothing had Bellerophon praised his intelligence also, for he put the sun behind him so that it shone straight into the Chimaera's eyes as they focused on him. When he dropped Bellerophon for once was not taken by surprise and was with the horse all the way. They hurtled downwards. The monster stayed motionless. The attack was accurate and deadly. At the turning-point of the dive Bellerophon struck cleanly, and although the shock of the impact made him reel, they were out of danger before the lion's head hit the rock and fell from there into the gulf. The Chimaera howled after it, and the head howled back. Bellerophon shuddered, and held his dripping sword clear of himself and his horse.

Pegasus, on the other hand, pranced and sidled in the air, behaving like himself again.

'Don't be frivolous,' said Bellerophon gently, checking him. 'Two more heads yet.' Pegasus, familiar with this reproof, was duly chastened, and started to gain height for the next dive. The Chimaera, realizing its peril, pressed itself against the mountainside. When it heard the air booming in Pegasus's wings as he dived the second time, it shrank back still further. This made everything more difficult. As the sword cut through the goat's neck it hit the rock behind and broke off a foot from the point. Pegasus's right wing and his tail were scorched by the fire that welled out of the stump of neck as he pivoted on the ledge, but they didn't catch alight. He swung clear as the second head followed the first.

The Chimaera now appeared smaller still, but more venomous. It wreathed itself in smoke.

'One more,' said Bellerophon jubilantly. 'We'll have to go in a bit closer next time, though.'

He and Pegasus had grown very sure of themselves, but the Chimaera was desperate. It turned at bay, and on the third dive it was ready for them. As they levelled out beside it for the last attack, it lunged off the solid rock, uncoiling and springing towards them ponderously but fluidly. Bellerophon was leaning over recklessly, and Pegasus dared not fling himself out of range. For a moment both creatures hung in space, and it seemed as if the air would not support the Chimaera, and that it would fall down between Pegasus and the ledge it had left, and hit the rocks far below. Then it jack-knifed in its own length, as a worm doubles up on itself when you touch it, straightened out and stretched itself with a jerk, and reached out to take a stranglehold with its forepaws on the flying horse. The three of them sank together through the gulf in a whirlwind of struggling and blows. Pegasus, lurching and foundering, flew hopelessly towards a little tarn about half a mile away, though he knew that they would all either have gone up in flames or crashed to the ground before they got anywhere near so safe a landing. He kicked like a catapult at the wriggling body of the Chimaera, and with a savage snap fixed his teeth in its neck, just behind the one remaining head. Bellerophon, snatching his feet out of the way of its fiery breath, found himself kneeling between Pegasus's wings, staring into the lidless eyes and open mouth of the snake's head, held fast as it was in Pegasus's jaws as if in a clamp. He seized his sword with both hands and drove the broken blade with all his strength down between the snake's fangs into its gullet. He leant back just in time as a blast of fire shot skywards. I should have struck through both sides of its mouth, he thought, and pinned them together. Too late now, the sword's stuck for good. Still, at least we'll take the brute with us, when we hit the ground and break ourselves in pieces.

But the monster was dead. Less than the height of a house roof from the earth its grip loosened, Pegasus unclenched his teeth, and the carcase fell away, the sword between its lips. It turned over once before it smashed down on a solitary boulder and lay humped over it, with its spine splintered and its limbs collapsed round it.

Pegasus bounced in the air as the weight left him, and then glided on for nearly a mile with Bellerophon sprawled across his back, until he came to rest in a meadow full of cows and sheep.

★   ★   ★   ★

The grazing beasts showed no signs of alarm, but came quietly up and gathered in a circle round the winged horse and his rider, and bowed their heads. Then they spread out and wandered off again. At least, that was how it seemed to Bellerophon. He dismounted, and walked unsteadily round Pegasus to see if he had any injuries. Pegasus started to follow him, so they walked drunkenly round each other a couple of times before Pegasus stopped, and shook himself stiffly. A few burnt plumes floated down, his tail was ragged, and he had some claw-marks in his neck, but that was all. Bellerophon's hands were torn from slipping on the rocks, and his feet were singed. Both of them were smeared with oily soot.

'I think, between us, we've done a really good day's work,' Bellerophon said muzzily, as he sat down on the grass.

'So do I,' said a girl's voice. Pegasus snorted. It was the daughter at the nearby farmstead. She had seen the final part of the battle, and had followed on foot to offer the victors her own breakfast. Where there has been a Chimaera, people wisely take everything for granted—or else, foolishly, take nothing on trust.

'Good day's work! It isn't even breakfast time yet,' she said, but her eyes shone. She gave Bellerophon a hunk of bread and cheese and an apple. 'Here's a piece of honeycomb for your horse.' She was accustomed to animals, but she looked cautiously at Pegasus. Even in weariness and grime his beauty was startling and his aspect full of glory. But he came hopefully up for his titbit, and sucked it out of her palm like a foal.

'You'll get toothache, you pampered jade,' said Bellerophon tenderly. Pegasus bent his head, took Bellerophon's apple out of his hand, and crunched it up.

'I think you're both heroes,' said the girl, laughing. 'I'll make you both garlands after I've done the milking. How is the king going to reward you?'

'His daughter's hand, I think,' said Bellerophon, with his mouth full. 'He didn't think I'd do it, you see. He didn't believe in Pegasus. I don't think he was too sure about the Chimaera either.' The girl didn't understand this. 'He just wanted to get rid of me. I wasn't in love with his daughter anyway, though I think I thought I was at the time.' She understood this. 'I'd forgotten all about her till now. It all seems so remote. I don't think I'll go back to the capital. The king will hear the news in his own good time, and the main thing is, the Chimaera's dead.' The girl, who had better reason than Bellerophon to know the importance of this, since she had lived for a long time under the shadow of the monster, nodded gravely. 'Anyway, I doubt if Pegasus would fancy a triumphal procession. He doesn't need telling how brave and clever he is—do you, greedy?' Pegasus put his head over Bellerophon's shoulder, took away his last mouthful of bread and cheese, mumbled it for a moment, and then dropped it back in his lap.

'Thank you!' said Bellerophon. 'I say, is there a stream nearby? I'm awfully thirsty.'

'Yes, but if you'd rather have milk there'll be some shortly. Lie still a minute, and I'll fetch my favourite cow and milk her into your mouth.'

She went off to collect a wooden pail and stool from under the hedge, and returned followed by a pretty little brindled cow, who stood quietly while her milkmaid settled herself with her head in her flank and milked one teat into the pail, and the other into Bellerophon's mouth, until he had had enough. Pegasus watched solemnly while he spluttered.

'Don't let him near the bucket,' Bellerophon warned, 'or he'll blow into it and spray the milk all over you.' But Pegasus trotted off to take his turn at the water trough.

'What are you going to do about him?' the girl asked quietly, changing on to the other two teats.

'Well, we'll probably go back to Helicon—the place where we met,' said Bellerophon, puzzled first by the question and then by the answer, which suddenly seemed to be not quite what he wanted. 'Actually, I'd rather stay here, but I expect he'd like to go back. It's his home, I think, if he has one. You know—I hadn't thought about it—he loves me, well, I love him just as much—but we'll have to part some day, I suppose.'

'You will,' the girl agreed. 'He's immortal.'

'So he is. Of course. I hadn't taken it in properly. Oh, Pegasus,' he said, softly and sorrowfully.

'Where's *your* home?' the girl asked quickly, hating to see him look so heartbroken at the thought of the parting.

'Nowhere, really. I've been wandering about most of my life. Now I've had one real adventure, I'd like to settle down, for good.'

'Doing what?'

'Oh, I don't know.' He watched her stripping the udders for the last drops, and grinned as an idea struck him. 'Is it easy to milk?'

She grinned back.

'It comes naturally to some. I'll bring the old white cow over to you and you can try and see.'

★   ★   ★   ★

When the milking was over and all the milk taken down to the farm, Bellerophon and the girl went back to the meadow and groomed Pegasus, for he hated feeling scruffy; and Bellerophon washed himself in the stream while the girl made garlands for the man and the horse, which they wore until the noonday sun withered them. Then the two humans lay and talked and talked in the shade until the evening, while Pegasus browsed round them. As the sun began to set the winged horse sprang into the air, and drifted among the darting swallows like a great white moth. Then he rose higher and set off westwards.

'Goodbye!' shouted Bellerophon suddenly. A distant, unmistakable neigh came back to him. The girl put her arms round him to comfort him.

'Was he jealous?' he said unhappily.

'No!' said the girl. 'But he must be given all your heart or nothing.'

'I'm afraid he'll be lonely,' said Bellerophon.

★　　★　　★　　★

For years Bellerophon would never ride an ordinary horse, even when he had married the girl, and had a son of his own, and the farmstead had prospered exceedingly under his hands, after the setbacks it had received while the Chimaera was alive. Then, one day, he saw his son gazing up at the sky, listening, with a white plume in his hand. Later he noticed grass-stains on the boy's tunic, and hoofprints that came and went in the dew. His wife remarked that honeycomb was always going from the larder.

'I think I'll get myself a little cob to ride round the pastures, instead of walking,' he thought. 'I'm not as young as I was, after all.'

There would always be someone who would find in Pegasus the companion he needed in adventure, after the winged horse had first learned, by making a friend of Bellerophon, to bestow his friendship among mortal men.

BAMBI AND THE OLD STAG

Felix Salten

Bambi, the young faun, had to learn that growing up is not always easy. . . .

Bambi was often alone now. But he was not so troubled about it as he had been the first time. His mother would disappear and no matter how much he called her she wouldn't come back. Later she would appear unexpectedly and stay with him as before.

One night he was roaming around quite forlorn again. He could not even find his cousins Gobo and Faline. The sky had become pale grey and it began to darken so that the tree-tops seemed like a vault over the bushy undergrowth. There was a swishing in the bushes, a loud rustling came through the leaves and Bambi's mother dashed out. Someone else raced close behind her. Bambi did not know whether it was Aunt Ena or his father or someone else. But he recognized his mother at once. Though she rushed past him so quickly, he had recognized her voice. She screamed and it seemed to Bambi as if it were in play, though he thought it sounded a little frightened too.

One day Bambi wandered for hours through the thicket. At last he began to call. He simply couldn't bear to be so utterly lonely any more. He felt that pretty soon he'd be perfectly miserable. So he began to call for his mother.

Suddenly one of the fathers was standing in front of him looking sternly down at him. Bambi hadn't heard him coming and was terrified. This stag looked more powerful than the others, taller and prouder. His coat shone with a deeper richer red, but his face shimmered, silvery grey. And tall black beaded antlers rose high above his nervous ears.

'What are you crying about?' the old stag asked severely. Bambi trembled in awe and did not dare answer. 'Your mother has no time for you now,' the old stag went on. Bambi was completely dominated by his masterful voice and at the same time, he admired it. 'Can't you stay by yourself? Shame on you!'

Bambi wanted to say that he was perfectly able to stay by himself, that he had often been left alone already, but he could not get it out. He was obedient and he felt terribly ashamed. The stag turned around and was gone. Bambi didn't know where or how, or whether the stag had gone slow or fast. He had simply gone as suddenly as he had come. Bambi strained his ears to listen, but he could not catch the sound of a departing footstep or a leaf stirring. So he thought the old stag must be somewhere close by and snuffed the air in all directions. It brought him no scent. Bambi sighed with relief to think he was alone. But he felt a lively desire to see the old stag again and win his approval.

When his mother came back he did not tell her anything of his encounter. He did not call her any more either the next time she disappeared. He thought of the old stag while he wandered around. He wanted very much to meet him. He wanted to say to him, 'See, I don't call my mother any more,' so the old stag would praise him.

But he told Gobo and Faline the next time they were together on the meadow. They listened attentively and had nothing to relate that could compare with this.

'Weren't you frightened?' asked Gobo excitedly.

O well,—Bambi confessed, he had been frightened. But only a little.

'I should have been terribly frightened,' Gobo declared.

Bambi replied, no, he hadn't been very much afraid, because the stag was so handsome.

'That wouldn't have helped me much,' Gobo added, 'I'd have been too afraid to look at him. When I'm frightened I have streaks before my eyes so that I can't see at all, and my heart beats so fast that I can't breathe.'

Faline became very thoughtful after Bambi's story and did not say anything.

But the next time they met, Gobo and Faline bounded up in great haste. They were alone again and so was Bambi. 'We have been hunting for you all this time,' cried Gobo. 'Yes,' Faline said importantly, 'because now we know who it was you saw.' Bambi bounded into the air for curiosity and asked, 'Who?'

Faline said solemnly, 'It was the old Prince.'

'Who told you that?' Bambi demanded.

'Mother,' Faline replied.

Bambi was amazed. 'Did you tell her the whole story?' They both nodded. 'But it was a secret,' Bambi cried angrily.

Gobo tried to shield himself at once. 'I didn't do it, it was Faline,' he said. But Faline cried excitedly 'What do you mean, a secret? I wanted to know who it was. Now we all know and it's much more exciting.'

Bambi was burning up with desire to hear all about it and let himself be mollified. Faline told him everything. 'The old Prince is the biggest stag in the whole forest. There isn't anybody else that compares with him. Nobody knows how old he is. Nobody can find out where he lives. No one knows his family. Very few have seen him even once. At times he was thought to be dead because he hadn't been seen for so long. Then someone would see him again for a second and so they knew he was still alive. Nobody had ever dared ask him where he had been. He speaks to nobody and no one dares speak to him. He uses trails none of the others ever use. He knows the very depths of the forest. And he does not know such a thing as danger. Other Princes fight one another at times, sometimes in fun or to try each other out, sometimes in earnest. For many years no one has fought with the old stag. And of those who fought with him long ago not one is living. He is the great Prince.'

Bambi forgave Gobo and Faline for babbling his secret to their mother. He was even glad to have found out all these important things, but he was glad that Gobo and Faline did not know all about it. They did not know that the great Prince had said, 'Can't you stay by yourself? Shame on you!' Now Bambi was very glad that he had not told them about these things. For then Gobo and Faline would have told that along with the rest, and the whole forest would have gossiped about it.

That night when the moon rose Bambi's mother came back again.

He suddenly saw her standing under the great oak at the edge of the meadow looking around for him. He saw her right away and ran to her.

That night Bambi learned something new. His mother was tired and hungry. They did not walk as far as usual. The mother quieted her hunger in the meadow where Bambi too was used to eating most of his meals. Side by side they nibbled at the bushes and pleasantly ruminating, went farther and farther into the woods.

Presently there was a loud rustling in the bushes. Before Bambi could guess what it was his mother began to cry aloud as she did when she was very terrified or when she was beside herself. 'Aoh!' she cried and, giving a bound, stopped and cried, 'Aoh! Baoh!' Bambi tried to make out the mighty forms which were drawing near as the rustling grew louder. They were right near now. They resembled Bambi and Bambi's mother, Aunt Ena and all the rest of his family, but they were gigantic and so powerfully built that he stared up at them overcome.

Suddenly Bambi began to bleat, 'Aoh! Baoh-baoh!' He hardly knew he was bleating. He couldn't help himself. The procession tramped slowly by. Three, four giant apparitions, one after the other. The last of them was bigger than any of the others. He had a wild mane on his neck and his antlers were tree-like. It took Bambi's breath away to see them. He stood and bleated from a heart full of wonder, for he was more weirdly affected than ever before in his life. He was afraid, but in a peculiar way. He felt how pitifully small he was, and even his mother seemed to him to have shrunk. He felt ashamed without understanding why and at the same time terror shook him. He bleated, 'Baoh! b-a-o-h!' He felt better when he bleated that way.

The procession had gone by. There was nothing more to be seen or heard. Even his mother was silent. Only Bambi kept giving short bleats now and then. He still felt the shock.

'Be still,' his mother said, 'they have gone now.'

'Oh, Mother,' Bambi whispered, 'who was it?'

'Well,' said his mother, 'they are not so dangerous when all is said and done. Those are your big cousins, the elk—they are strong and they are important, far stronger than we are.'

'And aren't they dangerous?' Bambi asked.

'Not as a rule,' his mother explained. 'Of course, a good many

Suddenly the Old Stag was towering over him.

things are said to have happened. This and that is told about them, but I don't know if there is any truth in such gossip or not. They've never done any harm to me or to any one of my acquaintances.'

'Why should they do anything to us?' asked Bambi, 'if they are cousins of ours?' He wanted to feel calm but he kept trembling.

'O, they never do anything to us,' his mother answered, 'but I don't know why, I'm frightened whenever I see them. I don't understand it myself. But it happens that way every time.'

Bambi was gradually reassured by her words but he remained thoughtful. Right above him in the branches of an alder, the screech-owl was hooting in his blood-curdling way. Bambi was distracted and forgot to act as if he had been frightened. But the screech-owl flew by anyhow and asked, 'Didn't I frighten you?'

'Of course,' Bambi replied, 'you always frighten me.'

The screech-owl chuckled softly. He was pleased. 'I hope you don't hold it against me,' he said, 'it's just my way.' He fluffed himself up so that he resembled a ball, sank his bill in his foamy white feathers and put on a terribly wise and serious face. He was satisfied with himself.

Bambi poured out his heart to him. 'Do you know?' he began slyly, 'I've just had a much worse fright.'

'Indeed!' said the owl, displeased.

Bambi told him about his encounter with his giant relations.

'Don't talk to me about relations,' the owl exclaimed, 'I've got relations too. But I only fly about in the daytime so they are all down on me now. No, there isn't much use in relations. If they're bigger than you are, they're no good to you, and if they're smaller they're worth still less. If they're bigger than you, you can't bear them because they're proud, and if they're smaller they can't bear you because you're proud. No, I prefer to have nothing to do with the whole crowd.'

'But I don't even know my relations,' Bambi said, laughing shyly. 'I never heard of them, I never saw them, before today.'

'Don't bother about such people,' the screech-owl advised. 'Believe me,' and he rolled his eyes significantly, 'believe me, it's the best way. Relatives are never as good as friends. Look at us, we're not related in any way but we're good friends, and that's much better.'

Bambi wanted to say something else but the screech-owl went on,

'I've had experience with such things. You are still too young but, believe me, I know better. Besides, I don't like to get mixed up in family affairs.' He rolled his eyes thoughtfully and looked so impressive with his serious face that Bambi kept a discreet silence.

*   *   *   *

Another night passed and morning brought an event.

It was a cloudless morning, dewy and fresh. All the leaves on the trees and the bushes seemed suddenly to smell sweeter. The meadows sent up great clouds of perfume to the tree-tops.

'Peep!' said the field-mice when they awoke. They said it very softly. But since it was still grey dawn they said nothing else for a while. For a time it was perfectly still. Then a crow's hoarse rasping caw sounded far above in the sky. The crows had awakened and were visiting one another in the tree-tops. The magpie answered at once, 'Shackarakshak! Did you think I was still asleep?' Then a hundred small voices started in very softly here and there. Peep! peep! tiu! Sleep and the dark were still in these sounds. And they came from far apart.

Suddenly a blackbird flew to the top of a beech. She perched way up on the topmost twig that stuck up thin against the sky and sat there watching how, far away over the trees, the night-weary, pale-grey heavens were glowing in the distant east and coming to life. Then she commenced to sing.

Her little black body seemed only a tiny dark speck at that distance. She looked like a dead leaf. But she poured out her song in a great flood of rejoicing through the whole forest. And everything began to stir. The finches warbled, the little redthroat and the goldfinch were heard. The doves rushed from place to place with a loud clapping and rustling of wings. The pheasants cackled as though their throats would burst. The noise of their wings, as they flew from their roosts to the ground, was soft but powerful. They kept uttering their metallic splintering call with its soft ensuing chuckle. Far above, the falcons cried sharply and joyously, 'Yayaya!'

The sun rose.

'Diu diyu!' the yellow bird rejoiced. He flew to and fro among the branches, and his round yellow body flashed in the morning light like a winged ball of gold.

Bambi walked under the great oak on the meadow. It sparkled with dew. It smelled of grass and flowers and moist earth, and whispered of a thousand living things. Friend Hare was there and seemed to be thinking over something important. A haughty pheasant strutted slowly by, nibbling at the grass seeds and peering cautiously in all directions. The dark metallic blue on his neck gleamed in the sun.

One of the Princes was standing close to Bambi. Bambi had never seen any of the fathers so close before. The stag was standing right in front of him next to the hazel bush and was somewhat hidden by the branches. Bambi did not move. He wanted the Prince to come out completely and was wondering whether he dared speak to him. He wanted to ask his mother and looked around for her. But his mother had already gone away and was standing some distance off, beside Aunt Ena. At the same time Gobo and Faline came running out of the woods. Bambi was still thinking it over without stirring. If he went up to his mother and the others now he would have to pass by the Prince. He felt as if he couldn't do it.

'O well,' he thought, 'I don't have to ask my mother first. The old Prince spoke to me and I didn't tell mother anything about it. I'll say, 'Good-morning, Prince.' He can't be offended at that. But if he does get angry I'll run away fast.' Bambi struggled with his resolve which began to waver again.

Presently the Prince walked out from behind the hazel bush on to the meadow.

'Now,' thought Bambi.

Then there was a crash like thunder.

Bambi shrank together and didn't know what had happened. He saw the Prince leap into the air under his very nose and watched him rush past him into the forest with one great bound.

Bambi looked around in a daze. The thunder still vibrated. He saw how his mother and Aunt Ena, Gobo and Faline fled into the woods. He saw how Friend Hare scurried away like mad. He saw the pheasant running with his neck outstretched. He noticed that the forest grew suddenly still. He started and sprang into the thicket. He had made only a few bounds when he saw the Prince lying on the ground in front of him, motionless. Bambi stopped horrified, not understanding what it meant. The Prince lay bleeding from a great wound in his shoulder. He was dead.

'Don't stop!' a voice beside commanded. It was his mother who rushed past at full gallop. 'Run,' she cried. 'Run as fast as you can!' She did not slow up, but raced ahead, and her command brought Bambi after her. He ran with all his might.

'What is it, Mother?' he asked. 'What is it, Mother?'

His mother answered between gasps, 'It—was—He!'

Bambi shuddered and they ran on. At last they stopped for lack of breath.

'What did you say? Tell me what it was you said?' a soft voice called down from overhead. Bambi looked up. The squirrel came chattering through the branches.

'I ran the whole way with you,' he cried. 'It was dreadful.'

'Were you there?' asked the mother.

'Of course I was there,' the squirrel replied. 'I am still trembling in every limb.' He sat erect, balancing with his splendid tail, displaying his small white chest, and holding his forepaws protestingly against his body. 'I'm beside myself with excitement,' he said.

'I'm quite weak from fright myself,' said the mother. 'I don't understand it. Not one of us saw a thing.'

'Is that so?' the squirrel said pettishly. 'I saw Him long before.'

'So did I,' another voice cried. It was the magpie. She flew past and settled on a branch.

'So did I,' came a croak from above. It was the jay who was sitting on an ash.

A couple of crows in the tree-tops cawed harshly, 'We saw Him, too.'

They all sat around talking importantly. They were unusually excited and seemed to be full of anger and fear.

'Whom?' Bambi thought. 'Whom did they see?'

'I tried my best,' the squirrel was saying, pressing his forepaws protestingly against his heart. 'I tried my best to warn the poor Prince.'

'And I,' the jay rasped. 'How often did I scream? But he didn't care to hear me.'

'He didn't hear me either,' the magpie croaked. 'I called him at least ten times. I wanted to fly right past him, for, thought I, he hasn't heard me yet; I'll fly to the hazel bush where he's standing. He can't help hearing me there. But at that minute it happened.'

'My voice is probably louder than yours, and I warned him as well as I could,' the crow said in an impudent tone. 'But gentlemen of that stamp pay little attention to the likes of us.'

'Much too little, really,' the squirrel agreed.

'Well, we did what we could,' said the magpie. 'We're certainly not to blame when an accident happens.'

'Such a handsome Prince,' the squirrel lamented. 'And in the very prime of life.'

'Akh!' croaked the jay. 'It would have been better for him if he hadn't been so proud and had paid more attention to us.'

'He certainly wasn't proud.'

'No more so than the other Princes of his family,' the magpie put in.

'Just plain stupid,' sneered the jay.

'You're stupid yourself,' the crow cried down from overhead. 'Don't you talk about stupidity. The whole forest knows how stupid you are.'

'I!' replied the jay, stiff with astonishment. 'Nobody can accuse me of being stupid. I may be forgetful but I'm certainly not stupid.'

'O just as you please,' said the crow solemnly. 'Forget what I said to you but remember that the Prince did not die because he was proud or stupid, but because no one can escape Him.'

'Akh!' croaked the jay. 'I don't like that kind of talk.' He flew away.

The crow went on, 'He has already outwitted many of my family. He kills what He wants. Nothing can help us.'

'You have to be on your guard against Him,' the magpie broke in.

'You certainly do,' said the crow sadly. 'Goodbye.' He flew off, with his family accompanying him.

Bambi looked around. His mother was no longer there.

'What are they talking about now?' thought Bambi. 'I can't understand what they are talking about. Who is this "He" they talk about? That was He, too, that I saw in the bushes, but He didn't kill me.'

Bambi thought of the Prince lying in front of him with his bloody mangled shoulder. He was dead now. Bambi walked along. The forest sang again with a thousand voices, the sun pierced the tree-tops with its broad rays. There was light everywhere. The leaves began to smell. Far above the falcons called, close at hand a woodpecker hammered as if nothing had happened. Bambi was not happy. He felt himself threatened by something dark. He did not understand how the others could be so carefree and happy while life was so difficult and dangerous. Then the desire seized him to go deeper and deeper into the woods. They lured him into their depths. He wanted to find some hiding place where, shielded on all sides by impenetrable thickets, he could never be seen. He never wanted to go to the meadows again.

Something moved very softly in the bushes. Bambi drew back violently. The old stag was standing in front of him.

Bambi trembled. He wanted to run away, but he controlled himself and remained. The old stag looked at him with his great deep eyes and asked. 'Were you out there before?'

'Yes,' Bambi said softly. His heart was pounding in his throat.

'Where is your mother?' asked the stag.

Bambi answered still very softly, 'I don't know.'

The old stag kept gazing at him. 'And still you're not calling for her?' he said.

Bambi looked into the noble, iron-grey face, looked at the stag's antlers and suddenly felt full of courage. 'I can stay by myself, too,' he said.

The old stag considered him for a while; then he asked gently, 'Aren't you the little one that was crying for his mother not long ago?'

Bambi was somewhat embarrassed, but his courage held. 'Yes, I am,' he confessed.

The old stag looked at him in silence and it seemed to Bambi as if those deep eyes gazed still more mildly. 'You scolded me then, Prince,' he cried excitedly, 'because I was afraid of being left alone. Since then I haven't been.'

The stag looked at Bambi appraisingly and smiled a very slight, hardly noticeable smile. Bambi noticed it, however. 'Noble Prince,' he asked confidently, 'what has happened? I don't understand it. Who is this "He" they are all talking about?' He stopped, terrified by the dark glance that bade him be silent.

Another pause ensued. The old stag was gazing past Bambi into the distance. Then he said slowly, 'Listen, smell and see for yourself. Find

163

out for yourself.' He lifted his antlered head still higher. 'Farewell,' he said, nothing else. Then he vanished.

Bambi stood transfixed and wanted to cry. But that farewell still rang in his ears and sustained him. Farewell, the old stag had said, so he couldn't have been angry.

Bambi felt himself thrill with pride, felt inspired with a deep earnestness. Yes, life was difficult and full of danger. But come what might he would learn to bear it all.

He walked slowly deeper into the forest.

FRIEND MONKEY HELPS THE SAILORS

P.L. Travers

There is no one kinder or more helpful than Monkey, but somehow other people don't always appreciate his help, and his kind deeds tend to end up in chaos—as in this episode, where he finds himself aboard a ship. His full story is told by P. L. Travers in Friend Monkey, *about which Margery Fisher has written: 'There is so much in this incomparable book. It is comedy on the highest plane—that is comedy with the indispensable note of amazement and melancholy. Above all it is grounded on myth. The elusive beauty and disturbing puzzles of Hindu myth have enriched the story of* Friend Monkey *and have made it a piece of literature to be enjoyed by young and old alike. Pamela Travers shows triumphantly in this book what she means when she says she does not only write for children.'*

The ship swung to and fro on the water, her white sails flapping in the breeze, like washing on a line.

'Ahoy, there!' bellowed the sailor's mates, as his laden boat drew nearer.

'Ahoy, yourselves, and let down the rope! My cargo's about to sink the boat.'

A rope ladder came snaking down, and up it, hand over hand, went the natty navy-blue figure. Two fat bundles were tumbled aboard, and the sailor began to huff and puff as he laboured up with the third.

'Funny,' he thought, as he heaved and panted. 'I'd have said they all weighed about the same, but this one—whew!—it's a blooming millstone. Out of my way, Young Napper,' he warned. 'If this load falls on top of you, we'll be short of a cabin-boy!'

But the skinny, gangling lad at the rail made no attempt to move. He was staring over the sailor's shoulder.

'W-what you got there, Mr Hawkes?' he stammered, pointing towards the sack.

'Yes, Barley,' echoed Fat Harry, the cook. 'What you been up to now, mate? I thought you was sent for cocoa-nuts.'

'And cocoa-nuts, Harry, is what I got. Round green fruit off a cocoa-nut tree, in case you never saw one!' Barley Hawkes was sarcastic.

'Well, take a look behind you, mate. You'll find you've got more than nuts.'

'More than nuts?' He turned his head. 'Well, I'll be—' But what he was going to be no one knew, for as he lowered the sack to the deck, Monkey came sidling from behind it, extending his paw palm-downward.

'So that's where you were!' said Barley Hawkes. 'And me thinking you'd hopped it! Well, you've got a cheek, I must say, boarding my boat without a ticket. And who requested your company, if I might be so bold to ask?'

Young Napper thrust himself between them.

'Don't go hurting him, Mr Hawkes! He's only a beast. He knows no better!'

'Yes, Barley. You let him be!' Fat Harry grabbed him by the arm. 'He's not done anyone any harm. Give him half a chance!'

'Hurt him? Me?' roared Barley Hawkes. 'You gone crazy, the two of you? Why should I hurt him? He's my pal!' He flung Fat Harry and Napper aside and bent to receive Monkey's proffered paw.

But Monkey was there no longer.

He was busily emptying the sacks and tossing cocoa-nuts into the air. Fat Harry caught one in his apron. Napper tucked two inside his blouse. The rest of the crew came running up, and Monkey darted about among them scattering nuts in all directions. One fell into the sea with a splash, another was caught in a coil of rope, and another tripped the Captain up as he entered on the scene.

'What's going on?' the Captain demanded. 'This is a ship, not a football field.' He glanced round disapprovingly at the litter on the deck. Then his eye fell on the furry shape, a whirling thing with a long tail and a cocoa-nut in its arms.

The Captain's face was a sight to see. He was both surprised and indignant.

'I sent you for cocoa-nuts, Mr Hawkes, not apes! You know the company's regulations. No pets allowed on the high seas!'

'Ay, ay, Captain. I know the rules. And I went for nuts, just like you said. It was him—' He jerked his head at Monkey. 'It was him that got them for me.'

'What? That hairy creature?' The Captain frowned.

'He did, sir, honest and hope to die. Shook the cocoa-nuts down from the trees when they wouldn't budge for me. But I never meant to bring him aboard. He must have stowed away on the boat when I turned my head away.'

'Well—' The Captain bent down to stare at Monkey and touched the outstretched paw. And Monkey, taking this for a welcome, thrust the cocoa-nut into his arms.

'Hurrrumph! Well, the thing seems to be tame enough. I'll make an exception just this once. But he'd better behave—I warn you, Hawkes —or he'll find himself stowed away right there!' He pointed downwards with his thumb. 'Right there in Davy Jones's Locker.'

Davy Jones's Locker is down at the bottom of the sea. All drowned things go there at last, men and ships and chests of gold. There is nothing deeper in the world than Davy Jones's Locker.

'Cross my heart,' said Barley Hawkes. 'He'll be helpful, sir, I promise!'

Oh, the rash promises of sailors! But how could Barley Hawkes have known—no tiger was there to bid him heed, no cautionary mynah bird—that the time would come when he would wish that Monkey had helped a little less?

★   ★   ★   ★

Meanwhile, Monkey was all agog and delighted with his new world. Fat Harry searched through his dwindling stores and found him a ripe banana. Young Napper sewed him a blue serge cap with half the name of the ship round the rim. *'London Ex—'* was all it said. For Monkey's head was far too small to accommodate the whole word. Not that it mattered, the men agreed. An animal, since it could not read, would never know the difference.

'There you are!' Young Napper exclaimed, as he set the cap at a jaunty angle. 'Now you're one of us. You're a sailor!'

Monkey, overwhelmed with joy, was about to reward him with half the banana, when the Captain's voice called from the stern and Napper was hailed to more pressing duties.

'Anchors aweigh!' the Captain ordered. And at once there was a rattle of chains, the pounding of feet along the deck, the thunder of sails as they took the wind—the usual orderly confusion of a vessel resuming her voyage.

But where was Monkey?

Everywhere!

The new sailor worked with a will, hiding things that everyone needed, dragging out others that nobody wanted. Once, he got under the Captain's feet, but the Captain mistook his leg for a rope and pitched him into a corner.

The ship moved, giving herself to the sea, her timbers creaking rhythmically like the sound of somebody breathing.

'Take a last look at your island, pal,' said Barley Hawkes to Monkey. 'We shan't get another sniff of land till we dock in London River.'

He turned to gaze at the sandy shore, edged with its shawl of jungle green and the hills rising behind it. But, to his surprise, he could not see them. There was nothing but endless ocean.

'Captain! There's something wrong to starboard. That cocoa-nut island—it's disappeared! Take a squint through the spy-glass, sir! Maybe you can see it.'

'Disappeared? Ridiculous!' The Captain put his glass to his eye. He took it away, rubbed the lens, and peered through it again.

'Preposterous! It must be there! And yet—' The Captain's voice was quiet. 'You're right! That island's gone.'

'But where would it go, sir? It couldn't just blow away—like smoke!'

'Wherever it's gone, I don't like it. It wasn't on the chart, remember. We came on it unexpectedly. I used to hear tales,' the Captain brooded, 'of islands that came and went. But I took them simply as sailors'

168

yarns. It's a bad omen, Hawkes,' he said, as he swung his glass in a wide circle, searching the empty sea. 'Great Stars!' he cried. 'What's that up there!'

'Not the island, sir, surely?' An island in the sky, thought Barley, was as useless as one that disappeared.

'No, no!' said the Captain, testily. 'There's something up there on top of the mast.'

It was Monkey.

He had seen Young Napper run up the rigging and—anxious, as always, to render assistance—had scrambled after him. Now he was hanging, feet over head, apparently urging his sailor friend to work in the same position.

'Stop it! Let go!' Young Napper yelled. 'You'll have us overboard!'

But Monkey clasped him around the waist and swung him away from the mast. Together they dangled aloft for a moment, with only the sea beneath them. But Napper, alas, was too heavy.

'I'm gone! I'm lost! Oh, me poor old mother!' He slipped from Monkey's circling arm and hurtled towards the water.

The Captain and Barley Hawkes waited, helplessly flinging out their arms, for the end of their cabin-boy. But just then the ship gave a lurch to starboard, a sail swung out in a puff of wind and caught him in its lap.

With a horrible screech of tearing canvas. Napper slid down the slope of the sail and landed on the deck. Monkey, with a single leap, was waiting there to greet him.

'Oh, let me die,' Young Napper moaned. 'All me bones are broken!' He pressed himself against the deck, grateful for its solidity after the nothingness of air.

'Well—if there's a bone that isn't broken, I'll break it myself, Young Napper!' The Captain, relieved of anxiety, could now give vent to his anger. 'Look at that sail, all ripped to ribbons! Bully beef and water for you, until it's properly patched. And don't let me find you wasting time playing with that ape. Get a rope and tie him up or we'll have him wrecking the ship!'

'Oh, please, sir, not to tie him up! Wild beasts don't like it. They pine away.'

'That wouldn't worry me,' said the Captain.

'But he's not to blame—it was me, Captain!' Young Napper searched for a plausible phrase. 'I was trying to be a monkey.'

'Then try to be a cabin-boy.' The Captain turned away.

'Ay, ay, then, sir.' Young Napper snivelled, scrambling to his feet. He searched through the treasures in his pocket and fished up a piece of string. Then he put out his hand for Monkey.

But Monkey had left the scene of disaster and was now perched on the ship's side, gazing at the sky.

'Leave it loose,' whispered Barley Hawkes, as they tied one end of the string to the rail and the other to Monkey's ankle. 'Don't let him think he's a prisoner.'

Monkey, however, had no such thought. The string, he assumed, was another gift. And since his friends were tying knots, it was clearly his duty to help them. So, in spite of their efforts to dissuade him, he lashed his own foot to the rail as though his life depended on it.

Having done that to his satisfaction, he turned to the sky again.

'What's he staring at?' said Napper, tilting back his head.

A shadow was moving over the ship, blotting out the sun.

'An albatross!' The sailors cheered. For to meet an albatross at sea is considered great good fortune.

'A lucky omen!' the Captain cried, his anger visibly melting.

'An omen with a catch though, sir. It's lucky, they say, unless you feed them. Once they've eaten the food of land—' Barley Hawkes gave a shudder. 'They follow and follow after the ship, till somebody from the land joins them. I know it, Captain! I've seen it happen.'

'Nonsense, Hawkes! That's an old wives' tale.' The Captain believed in old wives' tales, but he did not like to admit it. 'And who would feed it, anyway? An albatross gets its food from the sea.'

The great bird glided over the ship, dipping and swerving above the sailors in a kind of skiey dance. Now and then he would turn away as though he had seen enough. But each time he came winging back, swooping lower and lower. Then, suddenly, with a determined movement, he folded his black and white wings together and landed on the rail.

'He's looking for someone!' said Barley Hawkes, as the bird turned his head from side to side.

Fat Harry gave a sudden cry. 'He's looking for me! I know him now. It's my old mate, Sim Parkin! We lost him overboard in a gale, down by Santiago.'

Albatrosses, seamen believe, are really the souls of drowned sailors. The bodies of men who are lost at sea go down to Davy Jones. But the rest of them, their own true selves, fly up to the air as birds. How this happens nobody knows. And sailors, being superstitious, do not like to enquire.

'It *is* you, Sim—isn't it?' Fat Harry lumbered towards the rail.

'Of course it's not Sim Parkin, Harry!' The Captain stamped with impatience. 'Nor Tom Smith, nor anyone else. Now, all of you, get back to work. You're sailors, men, not bird collectors. I tell you, this will bring us luck. Fair winds. Smooth waters. You'll see.' He strode off down the deck.

The Captain had spoken no more than the truth, at least as far as he knew it. He had met with many an albatross. And each time the meeting had brought them luck.

But he had not reckoned with Monkey. There he sat, lashed to the rail, his dark glance moving back and forth from the cook to the brooding bird.

'I know you, Sim!' Fat Harry whispered. 'I know the squint in your left eye.'

The bird's slanting eyes flickered, and he reached out with his beak.

'No, no! You keep off, boy!' Fat Harry took a step backwards.

'If I let you touch me, that's the end. I'll find myself down there.' He nodded darkly at the sea.

The albatross withdrew his beak and hung his head on his breast.

'Don't take it hard,' Fat Harry pleaded. 'I can't help liking my bit of life. You did, too, remember, mate? But if you're lonely—well, I'm here. You can always drop in when you're passing. Hi! Hold off! You leave him be!' Fat Harry let out a warning yell.

Monkey—having decided, apparently, that the albatross was in need of help—was now helping the albatross. One paw was stroking the drooping head, the other pressing upon the beak a morsel of banana.

'Don't eat it, Sim!' Fat Harry wailed. But the warning came too late.

The albatross had sniffed the fruit and was gobbling it down. It seemed to satisfy something in him, for his head went up with a lordly toss. His squinting eye fell on Fat Harry with a dark, significant glance. His beak, half open, seemed to smile. Then, with a lift of his great wings, he gave himself back to the air. Once more he circled about the ship, his shadow falling on every face. And then he turned away. The sailors watched, half bewitched, as his shape grew small in the distance.

'He's had what he came for,' Fat Harry moaned, blubbering into his apron. 'A bit of food from the land he wanted. And why? Because he wants me, too.'

'Shut up, Harry, you're not dead yet. And maybe it's just a seaman's yarn.' Barley Hawkes tried to reassure him.

'No, no, it's only a matter of time. And it's him!' He shook his fist at Monkey. 'It's that dumb thing as who's to blame. Him and his old banana!'

'You won't tell the Captain?' implored Young Napper.

'Of course he won't tell,' said Barley Hawkes. 'Harry's a gentleman.'

'What? Me split on anyone to the Captain?' Fat Harry was deeply offended.

So they buttered him up and smoothed him down, and soon he was laughing again. Fat Harry was an optimist. His mate, Sim Parkin, would surely get him—of that he had no doubt. But not today. Tomorrow, perhaps. And tomorrow, he reminded himself, is something that never comes. So he waddled off to the ship's galley, planning a new kind of stew for supper—salt-beef, hard biscuits, and cocoa-nuts.

It was a success. Everyone had a second helping.

There was even a saucerful for Monkey, which he picked at, not because he liked it, but simply to gratify Young Napper.

They sat together in companionable silence, Monkey secure in his knots of string, Young Napper untidily sprawled beside him.

The constellations were out in the sky. The North Star, that brings all sailors home, was shining in the Great Bear's tail. A following wind filled the sails, and the labouring ship creaked and groaned as she thrust the waves behind her. It was a moment—such a one comes in every voyage—when sea and sky, ship and men were part of a single whole.

As for the Captain, he was full of high spirits. Up and down the deck he went, shouting important orders. 'Trim the sails! Square away!

Put the helm down! Put the helm up!' and other nautical expressions.

'You see, Hawkes, I was right!' He laughed. 'The bird has brought us luck!'

'Ay, ay, sir,' answered Barley Hawkes, exchanging a glance with Young Napper and hoping that this was indeed the case.

The Captain had forgotten—if he ever knew—that luck, like fruit, takes time to ripen. It doesn't happen all at once.

With ill luck it is just the same. . . .

★   ★   ★   ★

Hour by hour, on their steady course, the constellations moved. The sailors alternately slept and watched, as they ran before the wind.

But towards morning the wind fell. There was not a pocket of air in the sails. The ship lay becalmed upon the water, motionless as a model ship inside a whiskey bottle.

And to make matters worse, a thick mist rose up out of nowhere. No man could see his own hand. The sailors spoke to each other in whispers, like ghost talking to ghost.

The Captain took this sudden change as a personal affront. He had praised the weather and called it lucky, and the weather, far from appearing grateful, had turned and flouted him.

He stumbled along the invisible deck giving orders in a loud voice that the mist absorbed and muffled.

Once, something moved swiftly by him, brushing against his arm. 'Is that you, Hawkes?' he called sharply.

'No, Captain, I'm up in the bow.'

And again, as he passed beneath some rigging, his glass was knocked from his hand.

'Is that you, Napper?' the Captain bawled.

'No, sir, I'm in the galley with Harry.'

'Then who keeps bumping me, confound it?'

Barley Hawkes made a move in the mist. He would have to go and help the Captain. He put out a hand to feel his way and found in it a small warm paw.

And within the paw was the Captain's spy-glass.

Monkey had wearied of sitting still, gazing at the sea. It was all very

well when the stars were out. But now it was dark and misty. He knew
—he had learned it in the jungle—that mist was tricky, not to be
trusted. And where were his friends? In danger, perhaps? If so, they
would surely need his help. So he quickly untied the string from his
ankle and went to look for them.

Up and down the ship he hunted, using his tail as a sounding line.
He banged into this and knocked down that. And at last, after a long
search, he came upon one of his cronies.

'So it was you! I might have known it! Don't you ever know when
to stop? How can I save you from Davy Jones if you gallivant about
like this?' Barley Hawkes, exasperated, felt around in the dark with
his foot and came on a coil of rope. He seized Monkey by the scruff
of the neck and dumped him down inside it. 'Now you stay there!'
he whispered hoarsely. 'Or I'll scalp you—that's a promise!'

The coil of rope was like a nest, cleaner than the mynah bird's,
and not a sign of an egg. Monkey settled himself serenely, taking it
for granted that, as he had helped the mynah bird, he was now helping the
sailor. All that could be seen of him—if any eye could have pierced the
mist—was the flat top of his blue serge cap and the letters *London Ex*—.

Barley Hawkes felt his way forward.

'Your spy-glass, sir!' he said smartly, as the Captain loomed up beside
him.

'Great heavens, Hawkes, a glass can't fly! How did it get up here?'

'Dunno, sir.' Barley Hawkes was stolid. 'Funny things happen in the
mist.'

'Far too many funny things, if you ask me, Mr Hawkes.'

'But it's lifting, sir. I can see you clear.'

And, indeed, the mist, having done its worst, was now giving way
to the dawn. Ship and sailors appeared again as though from a
conjurer's hat.

'And about time, too,' The Captain grumbled. 'Now we must
whistle for a wind.'

Landlubbers find it hard to believe that a wind may be called as
one calls a dog. But for sailors it is a fact.

Barley Hawkes pursed his lips and whistled. And it seemed that the
sky sent back the sound—a high, shrill, screaming echo that ended in
a loud bang as something hit the deck.

It was a cannonball.

'Steady, lads!' the Captain shouted, as the seamen set up a wild commotion. 'Somebody's making a big mistake. They can't do this to us, men. We're not armed, we're a trading ship. Run up the white flag—that'll show them!'

'Shippa ahoy-a! Heave-a to-a!' Voices were calling across the water.

'What do they mean—Heaver Toer! We're hove to already! Where's my glass?'

'There's a ship standing off on the port side, sir. By the look of the crew, I think they're pirates.'

'Pirates, Hawkes? Have you gone mad? This is eighteen hundred and ninety-seven. There haven't been pirates in these seas for over fifty years!'

'Well, they're flying the Skull and Crossbones, sir. And they're putting off a boat—'

'You're right! It's unbelievable! My thundering stars, they're boarding us. All hands on deck!' the Captain roared, as a dozen pirates, brandishing knives, came swarming over the side.

'At 'em, boys!' the Captain ordered, seizing a pirate by the waist and sending him sprawling across the deck.

'Ay, ay, sir!' willing voices answered. And then the rumpus began. Bumps, bangs, curses, groans—all the pandemonium of a hand-to-hand shipboard battle. And the sailors got the best of it. They were all unarmed, but their blood was up. Pirates, indeed! They'd pirate them!

So the raiders were flung this way and that, into the scuppers, against the masts, moaning and sobbing and rolling their eyes. Daggers and cutlasses slipped from their hands, the deck resounded with falling bodies. At the end of the fray there was not one pirate standing upright. The sailors tied their hands with rope, propped them against the ship's side, and regarded them triumphantly.

They were, indeed, a poor lot—shabby, toothless, and skinny. A tatterdemalion remnant, perhaps, of the buccaneers of long ago.

The Captain eyed them with contempt. 'Well, what have you got to say for yourselves?'

'Notta spikka Angliss,' a pirate muttered, dejectedly shaking his head.

Not speak English? Great gods! Bad enough to be a pirate, worse

The monkey was perched on the ship's side, gazing at the sky.

to board a British vessel lawfully plying her proper trade, but not to speak English—! What could the world be coming to, the Captain clearly wondered.

'We'll deal with this riff-raff later, lads! In the meantime, we must celebrate. Harry, splice the mainbrace!'

Splicing the mainbrace on board ship means doubling each man's ration of rum. The custom is highly esteemed by sailors.

And soon there came from the ship's galley such a sound of junketing, such roars of laughter, such jollification, that a passer-by, had there possibly been one, would have said that the mainbrace had been spliced many times more than once.

'Down with all pirates!' the Captain was shouting. 'We'll take their ship in tow, hearties. It's treasure-trove and prize money for every man of the crew.' A loud cheer greeted the good tidings.

'Well, fill up once more and then to work!' The Captain held out his pannikin. And something that looked like a very small sailor filled it with rum from a keg.

The Captain stared. Was it possible? Apparently, it was.

'It's that ape again!' he said wrathfully. 'I thought I gave orders to tie him up! How did he get in here?'

Nobody knew—except Monkey.

Sitting in his coil of rope, he had heard the panting battle cries and assumed that the sailors and their friends were playing a rowdy game. Such things happened daily in the jungle. And so he joined the fun. He was here, he was there, he was everywhere. But in all that skelter of arms and legs no one had noticed an extra pair. And later, amid the jubilation, no one had noticed the extra sailor. So the extra sailor had busied himself with pouring out the rum.

'Well?' said the Captain, ominously.

'He *was* tied up, Captain, sir! I did it myself,' Young Napper declared.

'It's true, sir,' put in Barley Hawkes.

This rosy vision so cheered the Captain that he burst into a sailing song and held out his cup again.

'Cross my heart,' Fat Harry added. 'Trussed him up like a roast duck.'

'Then it must have been those damned pirates. They'll have set him free as they came aboard.' Napper, Hawkes, and Fat Harry glanced at each other but said nothing. There was nothing to be said.

'Well, he seems to be making himself useful. And he'd jolly well better, or there'll be trouble!' The Captain's voice sounded ferocious, but for once his bark was worse than his bite. He was far too full of his own good fortune to be worried by a mere monkey.

Think of it! He had captured a gang of bloodthirsty villains—not single-handed, but that was a detail—the last pirates, perhaps, in the world. And now he was a hero. Maybe, as well as the prize money, someone would give him a silver medal. They might even make a waxwork of him and put him in Madame Tussaud's.

This rosy vision so cheered the Captain that he burst into a sailing song and held out his cup again.

But Monkey was no longer there to fill it. He was now searching through the ship, looking for other friends to help.

And very soon he found them.

They were sitting on the deck in a row, each with his head on the next man's shoulder, dejected and forlorn.

Their eyes brightened when Monkey appeared, for any pirate, like any sailor, knows a keg of rum when he sees it. And since, to Monkey, a pirate was as thirsty as the next man, their spirits were shortly as bright as their eyes. Up and down the row he went, tipping the rum to every mouth until the keg was empty.

The strangers were obviously grateful. They nodded and smiled at him toothlessly and held out their fettered hands. And Monkey, at once, knew what was needed. He had been tied up himself.

So he quickly unloosed the knotted ropes, eagerly glancing from pirate to pirate, hoping to be of further service. But his new friends, it seemed, were about to depart. The only help they needed—or wanted —was a leg-up over the side. One by one, they tottered shakily to their feet and, with Monkey giving a heave and a push, clambered to the top of the rail and disappeared from view.

'Farewell and adieu to you, sweet Spanish ladies,' came the Captain's voice from the galley.

'*Farewell and adieu to you, ladies of Spain!*
Until we strike soundings in the channel of old England,
From Ushant to . . .'

The last words were drowned in a burst of applause. 'Up with the Captain!' somebody shouted. 'Down with the pirates!' cried another. And they clapped the Captain so hard on the back that they pushed him out of the crowded galley and followed him on to the deck.

It was just at this moment that the last pirate, courteously assisted by Monkey, clambered on to the rail.

Suddenly the rumpus ceased. The shouts died on the sailors' lips as they took in the situation. Even the sea was quiet.

For a second that seemed as long as a year, sailors and pirate stared at each other. Then the pirate took off his greasy cap and made a mocking bow.

'Gooda-bye-a! Olly vore! Ta ta!' He smirked. And with a hearty shove from Monkey, he was over and out of sight.

From below came the clonk and rattle of oars and a cackle of laughter, most un-English, as the pirates pulled away.

'Hawkes!' The word rang out like a shot from a gun.

'Ay, ay, sir,' muttered Barley Hawkes, who thought he knew what was coming.

The Captain pointed a trembling finger. His body shook with rage.

'Irons!' he spluttered. 'Put him in irons! Get that brute out of my sight. Take him below and clap him in.'

'Oh, not irons!' Young Napper wailed.

'It's that or drowning. Take your choice.'

'I could sew him up in a hammock, sir. He wouldn't escape, I promise.' Barley Hawkes reached out his arm for Monkey.

'TAKE HIM AWAY!' the Captain yelled. He was clearly beside himself. 'Sew him up, for all I care. Put him in chains! Strangle him! But if I set eyes on him again, you know what will happen, I warn you! He's brought nothing but trouble, trouble, TROUBLE, since the moment he came aboard.'

One cannot really blame the Captain. Being spick and orderly himself, he felt he had a right to expect that life should be orderly, too. Yet, here it was, all ups and downs, like a game of Snakes and Ladders.

He had found fresh cocoa-nuts, it was true, but he had lost an island. An albatross had brought him luck in the shape of a gang of pirates, and a wild beast, a thing from the jungle, had set the pirates free. No sooner, it seemed, was he up a ladder than he was down a snake. No one would give him a medal now, nor make a waxwork of him. The ill luck had indeed ripened.

As a last straw, it sent him a wind. Barley Hawkes had whistled for it, and the Captain had confidently expected a well-behaved, dependable breeze that would blow him gently home.

But what he got was a tornado.

It rose up out of nothingness, bellowing rudely through the rigging, ripping the sails into tatters. It flung the waves on top of each other till the sea, like a great watery whale, alternately swallowed the *London Exporter* and spat it out again. It even broke off the top of an iceberg and sent it into the Bay of Biscay, just where the ship was passing.

And always at the edge of the weather, round and round tirelessly, a dark shape flew and hovered. The sailors knew it was watching and waiting. But they did not tell the Captain.

Then, just as they entered the English Channel, the wind broke open the door to the galley where Fat Harry, bouncing from wall to wall, was trying to make a pudding. It sucked him out of his warm shelter and swept him on deck, shrieking for help. Then it picked him up, pudding and all, and tossed him into the sea.

'He should have been lashed to the stove,' said the Captain, as the waves closed over his body.

But no rope on earth, the sailors knew, could have lashed Fat Harry tightly enough to save him from his fate.

They were silent, staring down at the water. And the sea was suddenly silent, too. The wind changed from a roar to a whisper, the watery mountains flattened out, the iceberg turned tail and floated away. And the flying shape that had watched and waited lifted its wings triumphantly and flew towards the horizon.

'He knew it would happen, Harry did.' Young Napper wiped his nose on his sleeve. 'That there banana it was, what done it. And now Sim Parkin's got him.' He had no chance to finish what was evidently intended to be a long lament, for Barley Hawkes's hand was over his mouth.

'Hold your gob or I'll spiflicate you! Do you want the Captain to hear?'

He was thinking, of course, of Monkey and trying to save him, if he could, from Davy Jones's Locker.

But what was Monkey thinking?

There he lay, sewn up in his hammock, looking like an Egyptian mummy, with only his head uncovered. All through the storm, as the ship rolled over on her side or spun like a merry-go-round in the waters, he had seen the sailors tossed hither and thither and had longed to rush to their aid.

But no amount of twisting and turning could set him free from his canvas shroud. Barley Hawkes had done the job well. He couldn't even bite his way out, no matter how hard he tried.

Why had this happened, he asked himself. He had thought he was helping his new friends, and those same friends, far from being pleased, had sewn him up like a parcel.

He had never heard of Snakes and Ladders. But, nevertheless, it seemed to him that life was full of surprises. Up one minute and down the next with no one to tell him why.

So, since there was nothing else to do, he lay quite still and wondered.

And while he was busy doing this, the ship, egged on by a kindly breeze, came safely into port. . . .

ON A WING AND A PRAYER

Alan Coren

The largest known creature ever to have flown, an extinct reptile with an estimated wingspan of fifty-one feet, has been discovered by fossil hunters in West Texas. The creature had twice the wingspan of the biggest previously known pterodactyl.

The Times

From a hole in a rock just outside what was to become Sevenoaks, Homo Britannicus slowly emerged into the grey morning. A single snowflake floated down and settled on his forearm, paused, and dissolved among the thick, matted hair. He watched it disappear, his thin rim of forehead wrinkling.

A second landed on his broad flat nose. He squinted at it until it became a droplet, and until that droplet vanished.

'What's it like out?' called his wife, from the dark recess of the cave. H. Britannicus shivered.

'Bloody freezing,' he said. 'Also, promise you won't laugh, the rain is coming down in bits.'

His wife scuttled out, her lovely knuckles skimming the ground.

'What?' she said.

'Look,' he said. 'Bits.'

She looked at the snow, and she looked at the leaden sky.

'That'll be the Ice Age coming, then,' she said.

'Here,' said H. Brittanicus, 'what's that grey coming out of your mouth?'

'It's coming out of yours as well,' she snapped. 'How do I know what it is, I've never been in an Ice Age before, have I?'

H. Britannicus shook his head slowly. Tiny Pleistocene items flew out of his thatch, and hitting the chilly air, immediately became extinct.

'What's it all coming to?' said H. Britannicus. 'Where will it all end? When I was a kid, the summers we had!'

'I blame,' said his wife, 'the tool. All these bone needles, all these flint hammers, it's not natural.'

'Progress,' said her husband. 'You got to have progress.'

He tried to stand a little more erect. It wasn't easy.

'I'm off for a bit of a stroll,' he said. 'I'll catch me death standing here.'

★   ★   ★   ★

It was just outside what is now the subsoil of Canterbury that Homo Britannicus glanced up through his rime-hung eyebrows and noticed a figure shambling towards him. It had a pterodactyl on its arm.

'Morning,' said Homo Britannicus, taking a firmer grip on his club, just in case.

'Bonjour,' said the figure.

H. Britannicus raised his club slightly.

'What?' he said.

'Mah nem,' said the figure, 'eez Omo Gallicus. 'Ow eez eet going?'

'Mustn't grumble,' said Homo Britannicus. 'Where are you from?'

Homo Gallicus pointed behind him with his free hand, towards France.

'Ah 'ave walk many days,' said Homo Gallicus, 'wiz a proposition.'

'It looks like an ordinary bloody pterodactyl to me,' said Homo Britannicus. 'And what's that round your neck?'

'Wi call zem onions,' said Homo Gallicus.

Homo Britannicus reached out and felt one, cautiously.

'You'll never kill nothing with that, son,' he said. 'Too soft.'

'Wi eat zem,' said Homo Gallicus.

Homo Britannicus looked at him.

'It takes all sorts,' he said. 'What's the pterodactyl for?'

'Where can wi talk?' replied Homo Gallicus.

They found a small cave, and crept inside, and sat down. Homo Britannicus blew on his fingers.

'I wish we had a couple of sticks,' he said.

'What for?'

Homo Britannicus thought for a while.

'I'm not sure,' he said, at last. He nodded towards the pterodactyl. 'What about him, then?'

'In mah country,' began Homo Gallicus, 'wi 'ave no dinosaurs. Zer dinosaur eez—'ow you say?'

'Extinct.'

'Exactement! 'Owevaire, wi 'ave zer pterodactyl. You, on zer uzzer 'and, 'ave no pterodactyl, but you 'ave zer dinosaur, n'est-ce pas?'

'Just a few,' said Homo Britannicus. 'They're a bit bloody ropey, mind. Past their best, know what I mean? We've let 'em run down, werl, there's no call for 'em these days, is there?'

'Ah beg to diffaire,' said Homo Gallicus. He bent forward, and his black eyes glittered. 'Mah plan eez to mate zer Gallic pterodactyl wiz zer Brittanic dinosaur! Wi will produce zer Gallo-Britannic pterosaur, mon vieux! Eet weel be zer biggest flying objeck evaire seen!'

'So what?'

'Zer Ice Age is coming, hein?' said Homo Gallicus. 'In an eon or two, eet will be 'ere. Wi weel 'ave to find warmaire climate, or . . .' he drew a thick finger across his imperceptible neck. 'Wi cannot walk, eet eez too far; so wi weel climb aboard zer giant pterosaur—*an' wi weel fly there!*'

'Gerroff!' cried Homo Britannicus.

'Also,' continued Homo Gallicus, unruffled, 'wi weel rule zer worl'! Everyone weel want one. Wi weel clean up zer pterosaur market.'

Homo Britannicus, to be fair, did all he could to fathom this momentous idea: he furrowed his millimetric brow, he scratched his craggy head, he sucked his great green teeth. But it was not until Homo Gallicus began to draw upon the cave-wall with his easy, flowing line, that his partner-to-be was really convinced.

It looked wonderful, in the picture.

★   ★   ★   ★

Over the next five years, the innumerable, unforseeable technological problems came forth and multiplied.

For two years alone, the dinosaur and the pterodactyl could not be persuaded to mate at all, and the wretched co-partners were forced to stand by while the two halves of the project shrieked and bit one another. But in the third year, by a process of strategic starving, feeding and cajoling, the message got gradually through, and the dinosaur fell pregnant.

Ultimately giving birth to an enormous saurian cylinder with six legs and two very small wings. It flapped these latter for a few impotent beats, fell over, and expired.

'Ah well,' said Homo Gallicus, 'back to zer cave-wall!'

Which was all very well, except that the family of Homo Britannicus was finding it more and more difficult to make ends meet: it was not merely that most of their breadwinner's time was spent in husbanding the animals involved, but also that those animals were consuming a vast amount of food. They were being saved from natural extinction only at the expense of the unfortunate hominids who had been forced to cast their lot with them.

'You never told us it would cost this much,' was how Homo Britannicus's wife put it, over and over again.

Whereupon her husband would flatten her with his club, a gesture which over the years was becoming less and less affectionate.

But towards the end of the fifth year (by which time the temperature had dropped to a constant ten below zero, and the emaciated families of the luckless inventors reduced to gnawing for nourishment upon the misshapen bones of past failed experiments), a small pterosaur was produced of rather pleasing proportion. Even more encouraging was the fact that when it flapped its large feathery wings, it actually took off, flew for a few yards, and landed again without breaking anything.

'It works!' shrieked the two Homos, hugging one another and dancing great whorls in the encircling snow. 'A new dawn is breaking!'

'Erk,' went the baby pterosaur. It opened its mouth wide. 'Erk.'

'Eet wants,' said Homo Gallicus, 'to be fed.'

★   ★   ★   ★

The two of them rejoiced when they saw it could fly.

For five more years they fed it, while it grew bigger and bigger. The cold wind that continued to blow through Europe having taken its constant toll, the vegetation was now so sparse that the family of Homo Britannicus spent its every waking hour in scouring the white landscape for pterosaur fodder, they themselves subsisting on grubs and bits of bark and anything else the pterosaur could not use.

'When will it be big enough?' they would plead of the manufacturers, 'when will it be ready? When will it all end? When will the miracle begin?'

And the manufacturers, by now mere hirsute skeletons themselves, would say 'Soon, soon.'

And then, in the bleak autumn of the tenth year, when its wingspan had reached fifty-one feet, and its sleek giant body was consuming a field a day, and its insistent 'ERK! ERK!' had reached a pitch and volume that would start avalanches rolling a dozen leagues away, they trundled the Gallo-Britannic pterosaur out of its enormous cave, and announced that it was ready.

'Wi weel head West,' cried Homo Gallicus, 'to zer sun and zer fleshpots!'

Homo Britannicus clubbed his wife for the last time, tenderly.

'Back in two shakes,' he said, and gathering the mangy ratskins about his jutting bones, he and his colleague climbed aboard.

The great wings flapped, and the pterosaur lumbered down the runway in a trail of webby pot-holes, and took off.

The last thing they saw, before the freezing snow-clouds enfolded them, was the pitiful little knot of rags beneath, staring upwards.

They seemed to be praying.

★ ★ ★ ★

It was warm in the place that was subsequently Dallas.

A group of fat, balding hominids were sitting around a triceratops-shaped pool, examining a roughly circular rock that Homo Texus was rolling up and down.

'I agree,' said Homo Oklahomus, who had made the trip especially to see it, 'it could be very big. It could be, like, very big indeed.'

'With the right packaging,' said Homo Arkansus.

187

'With the right packaging,' said Homo Oklahomus, nodding.

It was at that point that the sun was blotted out.

'What the—!' cried Homo Texus, letting the wheel roll from his fingers.

They leapt up, as the pterosaur came in to a perfect two-point landing, and ran across. Homos Gallicus and Britannicus jumped down.

'This is private property, buddy!' shouted Homo Texus.

'And this,' cried Homo Britannicus, 'is the Gallo-Britannic pterosaur! It will revolutionize travel, it will open up whole new experiences, it will . . .'

'The hell it will!' shrieked Homo Texus.

'Did you hear the goddam noise?' screamed Homo Oklahomus.

'My God!' yelled Homo Arkansus, pointing a trembling finger, 'look at its damn droppings!'

'The environment!' howled the Americans, 'The environment!'

Whereupon, brushing aside the enfeebled European bonebags, they fell upon the hapless pterosaur, and beat it to death.

Acknowledgements

The publishers gratefully acknowledge permission to reproduce the following stories and extracts:

ADOLF by D.H. Lawrence. Reprinted by kind permission of Laurence Pollinger Ltd. and the Estate of Frieda Lawrence Ravagli.

THE PIPER AT THE GATES OF DAWN from *The Wind in the Willows* by Kenneth Grahame. Reprinted by kind permission of Methuen Children's Books.

THE MIRACLE CLIMB from *Two in a Bush* by Gerald Durrell. Reprinted by kind permission of William Collins Sons & Co. Ltd.

MAXWELL'S OTTER from *Ring of Bright Water* by Gavin Maxwell (Penguin Books, 1974). Copyright © Gavin Maxwell, 1960.

THE LITTLE MILITARY LEARNED HORSE by Joan Selby-Lowndes. Reprinted by kind permission of The Lutterworth Press.

A WHITE HORSE WITH WINGS by Anthea Davies. Reprinted by kind permission of Faber and Faber Ltd.

BAMBI AND THE OLD STAG from *Bambi* by Felix Salten. Reprinted by kind permission of the author, translators Whittaker Chambers, and Jonathan Cape Ltd.

FRIEND MONKEY HELPS THE SAILORS from *Friend Monkey* by P.L. Travers. Reprinted by kind permission of William Collins Sons & Co. Ltd.

ON A WING AND A PRAYER by Alan Coren. Reprinted by kind permission of Alan Coren.

The publishers have made every effort to trace copyright holders. If we have omitted to acknowledge anyone, we should be most grateful if this could be brought to our attention for correction at the first opportunity.